636.932
Medow
THE CHINCHILLA

COP 3

OCT 1 '70 TEHACHAPI		
APR 5 '71 BAKER		
DEC 28 '76 Bookmobile	McKITTRICK	
APR 22 '77		
JAN 26 '79 ISABELLA		
JUL 30 1991 KRV		

The Chinchilla

by

HAROLD MEDOW

Published By:

THE TOZER CO.
Redwood City, California

CONTENTS

I. INTRODUCTION II
About the author
Search for information
Purpose of book

II. BIOGRAPHY OF THE CHINCHILLA 1
South American Origin
How the chinchilla nearly became extinct
Mathias F. Chapman's introduction of the
    chinchilla into the United States

III. START OF CHINCHILLA RANCHES 12
First sale of pelts
Beginning of breeders' and sales' organizations

IV. THE CHINCHILLA 22
Types of chinchillas
Physical characteristics
Chinchilla rats and mice
Quality

V. HOUSING 34
Cages
Temperature and humidity control
Sanitation
Different types of housing

VI. NUTRITION 60
Types of feed. Pellets, hay
Digestive system
Sanitation, water, feed, hay, storage, utensils

VII. HANDLING AND CARE 71
Observation
Schedules: feeding, watering, cleaning cages
Physical handling
Importance of regular schedules, environment

CONTENTS (continued)

VIII. BREEDING 83
    Monogamous, polygamous
    Pregnancy
    Care of young

IX. PRIMING 108
    Cages
    Temperatures
    Determining prime

X. PELTING 121
    Steps in pelting
    Care in handling
    Shaping

XI. FUR DRESSING 152
    Chinchilla fur
    Processing
    Brighteners

XII. MARKETING 164
    Organizations
    How they assist ranchers
    Pelt identification

XIII. RECORD KEEPING 173
    Animal records
    Importance of keeping accurate records
    Bookkeeping, taxes

XIV. GENETICS 186
    Systems of breeding
    Advantages and disadvantages of various
      types of breeding
    Herd improvement

XV. ARTIFICIAL INSEMINATION 194
    Benefits of semen evaluation
    Purpose of artificial insemination

XVI. DISEASES ....
    Causes, symptoms, suggested treatment,
      prevention

DEDICATION

*To my wife, Eva Medow,
whose assistance and devotion helped make this book possible.*

Chapter I INTRODUCTION

THE CHALLENGE OF A STORY

The chinchilla might well be called the animal of miracles. There was magic in its initial discovery and more magic in its survival to the present day after near extinction.

It is possible to say that every book has a story in it, and equally possible to say there is a story in the development of every book.

The author-photographer of this book discovered the chinchilla by chance on a news assignment for a daily newspaper. The fascination of the chinchilla story and its continuing development became nearly an obsession.

The interest in the original picture story led to a search for information and pictures over several years.

My role as a photographer on a newspaper changed to that of the editor of *Chinchilla Progress*. As the editor of this publication I realized the tremendous challenge and opportunity of gathering from many sources the material for this book.

The search for material and the chance to take pictures has taken me to many places from a Benedictine Monastery in the hills of California to the busy Fur Market of New York.

It has been a process of spending long and pleasant hours sharing the experiences of owners of chinchilla ranches, large and small.

At first it seemed a disadvantage to the author not to be actively engaged in the raising of chinchillas. As the book developed, however, it became in part an advantage. There are many differing methods used in raising chinchillas. Naturally, every rancher chooses those practices which seem best to him.

To provide a book on chinchillas, it is surely desirable to bring together the many alternatives.

It would be foolish for any author to claim that he has completely covered the field in reporting on chinchillas. However, this publication brings together many different facets of this fascinating industry.

This book has several purposes. It is hoped parts of it will be interesting to the general reader. A goal of equal importance has been to gather information of value to persons who are raising chinchillas and for those who plan to enter the field.

The author hopes this book will provide for the reader an understandable text, with clear illustrations on the chinchilla and on chinchilla ranching.

Naturally a book of this type is not really the work of one person. It is the result of the generosity of the many persons in all parts of the industry who have so willingly shared time and rich experience in making material available.

The chinchilla industry has gone through stormy periods. Some of these have been caused by the rarity of the chinchilla, and some by the zeal of a few unscrupulous opportunists who traded on the public's lack of information.

While the author firmly believes in the vital role of the chinchilla ranching industry and in its future growth, he has been concerned by the few instances he found where the uninformed had been victimized.

It is to the credit of the industry that there are many working through the federal government and through voluntary organizations to assure the sound ethical future of chinchilla raising.

If this book can help the uninformed, as well as provide an exchange of information among those participating in the industry, it will have amply rewarded the author's effort.

MATHIAS F. CHAPMAN

Mathias F. Chapman, founder of the chinchilla industry, died in 1934 at the age of fifty-two.

Chapter II   BIOGRAPHY OF THE CHINCHILLA

The rich, soft beauty of the chinchilla's fur has made his history the companion of royalty and the very wealthy since the days before Columbus. His furs formed part of the spoils of two wars.

There is irony in this turbulent history, for the chinchilla is a graceful, timid animal coming from the giant ranges of the Andes in Chile, Peru, Bolivia and Argentina.

About one-third the size of a rabbit, the chinchilla looks more like a squirrel, although he has big round ears, which have earned him the name, Orejuda, (Mr. Big Ears) in Chile. His tail is long and furry like that of the chipmunk.

Part of his charm comes from his big round eyes that often seem to be without pupils, looking somewhat like those of a deer.

His importance to man, however, comes from his fur. It is a lustrous blue-gray, an inch or more deep. It is tremendously dense, with from 50 to 100 or more hairs coming from a single follicle, and so silky that it can be rippled by a light breeze.

By choice the chinchilla lives in a rocky den in the semi-desert climate of the high Andes. It is assumed that the animals were monogamous by nature.

1

Man's first capture of the chinchilla is buried in the shadows of history. It is known that hundreds of years before Columbus discovered America the chinchilla was trapped by the Chincha Indians.

The Indians valued him for food and delighted in robes made from his soft fur. They also wove a silky cloth from his hair.

When the Incas became the overlords of the Chincha Indians, the chinchilla became a spoil of victory. The chinchilla fur robe took its place along with the brilliant feather weaving in the ceremonial robes of these ancient rulers of South America.

In 1527, when the conquistadores, led by Francisco Pizarro conquered the Inca empire, the chinchilla robes again became booty.

It is told that a chinchilla robe sent to Queen Isabella of Spain set court fashions, and it appears in records of the period that the chinchilla's fur accompanied the hoard of gold and silver carried by the galleons home to Spain.

From the time of the conquistadores the hunt was on and chinchilla became one of the prized, rare furs of the earth.

This was nearly the undoing of the chinchilla. By 1899 South American countries were exporting more than half a million pelts a year. Chile alone exported 435,463 pelts during that year.

The trapping of the chinchilla and this wholesale slaughter for his fur was taking its toll. By 1905 Chilean exports had dropped to less than 250,000; by 1910 to 150,000; and to about 3,000 in 1915.

Frederico Albert was one of the first chinchilla conservationists. In the late 1880's he published a periodical called *La Chinchilla*. His efforts to save the chinchilla from becoming extinct continued on into the early 1900's. Albert apparently was one of the first to stimulate laws restricting the trapping of chinchillas. However, it is obvious that these laws were not enforced, because the wholesale trapping of chinchillas continued.

The dark area shown on the map indicates regions where the chinchilla was found.

CHINCHILLA PELTS EXPORTED FROM CHILE

YEAR	NUMBER
1895	184,548
1896	321,375
1897	147,468
1898	332,328
1899	435,463
1900	370,800
1901	385,170
1902	126,940
1903	144,000
1904	314,100
1905	247,836
1910	152,863
1915	3,202
1917	4,380
1918 (export forbidden)	

The disappearance of the once bountiful chinchilla alarmed the South American governments—Chile, Peru, Bolivia, and Argentina. By 1918 all of them had placed an embargo on export of chinchilla furs, and had instituted laws against trapping the animal.

It was nearly an instance of too little action, too late. The resource was exhausted commercially for the nations involved.

Chinchillas might well have become scattered footnotes in history, except for the curiosity of an American mining engineer, Mathias F. Chapman.

Chapman, in recounting his interest in the chinchilla, noted his first contact with the animal was virtually an accident.

A Chilean Indian carried the first chinchilla Chapman saw into his camp one day in 1918. A lover of animals, Chapman was appalled to find that the animal, trapped in a five-gallon tank, had had little food and no water for more than two weeks.

It would appear that the chinchilla drank no water, for water was practically nonexistent in his natural habitat. It would seem that a bio-chemical manufacturing process of water by the animal was made possible by the starchy foods in the diet plus the air breathed by the animal, such as in the kangaroo rat.

Comparison (magnified) between a human hair and that of the chinchilla.

The chinchilla has from 80 to 100 or more hairs growing from a single follicle.

4

Perhaps the only logical explanation for the chinchilla's consumption of water today is that he is an adaptable animal. Chapman was almost a naturalist by avocation, becoming interested in animals wherever his work in engineering took him. This first contact with a chinchilla triggered the idea for a domestic industry. It wasn't an easy start, however.

Chapman's records show a search for chinchillas in 1919: "A party of twenty Indian trappers combed the mountains for three years to get a dozen suitable animals for Chapman. During that period some of the Indians didn't even see a chinchilla."

Excerpts from Chapman's diary are revealing on the difficulty encountered:

In October of 1921 Chapman notes: "Manuel Gonzales sent word that he had caught a pair of chinchillas. He had been after them for me for a long time, but somehow couldn't get any alive. I was rather anxious to see them, so I rode up to his place this morning. He had them in a powder box and they seemed to be quite wild. After putting on his gloves, he reached in for them. He said that the female is the larger and wider of the two and will have babies in a little while. I hope she has five or six for it seems to be so difficult to get them wild."

In this hope Chapman was naturally to be disappointed. A later diary entry notes: "Maggie (they had named the female this) had a baby last night. Nan (Mrs. Chapman) found it today. She had just one and it can see and wobble around a little. It has hair and looks like a spider and walks so funny—kind of jumps along and squeaks like a mouse. . ."

Chapman's diary is full of his discoveries, all of them naturally pioneering in raising chinchillas. He notes they were feeding them bread and lettuce and that they liked sugar. He also noted he was giving them water, although some of the native workmen said this would kill them.

Once having obtained the animals high in the Andes, it is believed Chapman began his journey back to the United States in easy stages, to acclimate the animals to lower altitudes.

Mathias F. Chapman's camp, high in the Andes Mountains. Photograph taken in 1921.

Mathias F. Chapman used this cage to hold the twelve chinchillas on the voyage from South America to the United States aboard the Japanese freighter, Anya Maru. A compartment in the center of the cage was filled with ice to protect the animals from the intense heat.

Collecting the animals and bringing them down from the high altitude was only the initial stage in Chapman's long Odyssey.

He won reluctant permission to take the live animals out of the country after a long period of negotiation and what seemed to him endless red tape.

Once released from the country, Chapman had to argue with the Japanese sea captain to keep him from putting the animals below decks where they were certain to die from the heat.

Chapman arrived in the United States at San Pedro, California on February 23rd, 1923, aboard a Japanese freighter. The chinchillas were then moved to 1629 West 84th Street in Los Angeles. In 1926 the animals were moved to Inglewood, California.

Four females and eight males survived the trip to become the major ancestors of the domesticated chinchillas in the world today. Although there have been later importations, none of them were as important as the original animals Chapman brought to the United States.

UNITED STATES DEPARTMENT OF AGRICULTURE
BUREAU OF BIOLOGICAL SURVEY
WASHINGTON, D. C.

ADDRESS REPLY TO
CHIEF, BUREAU OF BIOLOGICAL SURVEY,
AND REFER TO
EI-F
Chinchillas

April 19, 1923.

Mr. M. F. Chapman,
c/o Hellman Commercial Trust & Savings Bank,
6th & Main Sts., Los Angeles, Calif.

Dear Sir:

I note from the records in this office that the shipment of 12 chinchillas for which a permit was issued on January 11, arrived from Chile and was duly entered at the port of Los Angeles on February 21.

Will you kindly advise us as to the condition in which these animals arrived, the number of each sex, and where the experiment of breeding them will be conducted? As this is the first importation of these animals into the United States, at least for many years, the entry is one of unusual interest and we should be glad to know any details in regard to the project.

Very truly yours,

W C Henderson

Acting Chief of Bureau.

Chapman's chinchilla venture was the beginning of the Chinchilla Ranching Industry.

All of the furs which gave chinchilla its initial reputation had been trapped furs. The drastic reduction in the number of South American animals ended trapping as a source for all time.

There were efforts to revive chinchillas in the wild on the part of several of the governments, including Chile. However, none of these was successful at that time.

Before turning to a discussion of chinchilla ranching, it is an interesting sidelight to note that there are in fact a few wild chinchillas in the Andes today.

Among those studying the existence of the chinchilla in the wilds was Fritz Ferger of La Paz, Bolivia. In the late 1920's he trapped chinchillas and successfully raised them.

LOS ANGELES

INGLEWOOD

The first chinchilla ranch was in Los Angeles, California, at 1629 W. 84th Street. The building was a six pen structure. The pens had wooden floors. The building had a double roof. The second roof shaded the first roof, which had a cooling effect. (Photograph taken in 1925). In 1925 the ranch was moved to Inglewood, California, and located on the corner of Osak and Palm Streets. (Photograph taken in 1929). From Inglewood the animals were moved to Tehachapi, California. (Photograph taken in 1931).

TEHACHAPI

Chapter III   START OF CHINCHILLA RANCHES

So the wild chinchilla as a source of fur had vanished, never to be significant again. Only from the origin of the domesticated ranch chinchilla has the highly desirable gray-blue fur again become available.

Chapman's ranch in Inglewood, California was to become the source for a regeneration of the world's chinchilla population.

The four females and eight males were steadily bred to produce breeding offspring. There was, of course, no deliberate initial pelting. The only pelting was in the case of accident or disease.

The first sale of animals by the Chapman Farms took place in 1931. At that time 10 pairs of animals were sold under a pool arrangement for $32,000. This made each pair worth $3,200. Under this initial arrangement, interests of 1/32nd were sold.

It was projected that the animals would increase at a rate of 100 percent per year. It was intended that at the end of five years, each interest would equal one pair of chinchillas. The pool animals were maintained at Chapman Farms. A similar sale took place in 1932.

This building housed Mathias F. Chapman's sales office.

In this period speculation in chinchillas attracted a wide variety of people, many of whom had no intention of raising the chinchillas themselves. They were considered an investment in much the same way as a security.

The first full pair sold by Chapman was the 40th female and the 44th male born in captivity, purchased by W. J. Burns of Rochester, New York in 1934.

Chapman Chinchilla Sales Inc., was formed in 1935 to sell animals from the Chapman stock. Sales continued to be for fractional and full pair interests in pools. The pool animals were placed on ranches under the supervision of the sales company and in care of one of the pool's investors. The price continued to be $3200 a pair. A monthly ranching charge was paid by investors to the ranchers.

Offspring from the pools were sold back to Chapman Chinchilla Sales Co. for $1600 a pair.

The first full pair of chinchillas was sold in 1934 to W. J. Burns of Rochester, New York. The pair included the fortieth female and the forty-fourth male born in captivity. The photograph would indicate that the Burns' venture was quite fruitful.

These fantastically high values reflected the scarcity of chinchillas at the time. Regardless of quality, chinchillas were sold at $3200 per pair. (It is worth noting that until the second significant sale of chinchilla pelts in 1954, (sponsored by the Farmers Chinchilla Cooperative Association) no one knew the value of chinchillas, either as breeding stock or pelts.)

The single price for chinchillas was maintained by those early raisers operating in cooperation with the Chapman interests through 1941, although there was considerable pressure for a price reduction.

The coming of World War II took the matter out of the stage of argument and the price was lowered to "not less than $2000 per pair." However, some individual ranchers were more flexible. There was virtually no new interest during the war years.

Over these years, there had been gathered a number of casualty pelts by the National Chinchilla Breeders Association, a pioneer breeders' association. It was determined to hold an auction sale of these pelts with the goal of establishing a price for pelts which might be relied upon.

The separation of ownership of chinchillas and ranching and the lack of an established standard of value for chinchillas set the stage for some of the most heartbreaking events in the history of the chinchilla industry to those with unrealistic expectations.

Speculation in chinchillas as a kind of futures market (with astronomical guesses as to future value of pelts) opened the door to many shoddy promotions. Practically every community has some family that was "burned" by the prospect of fantastic profits in owning chinchillas.

In 1940 a census of the industry showed there were 1,000 owners of the 6,000 animals then known to be in existence. This ratio of six animals to each owner is deceptive when we feed into it the knowledge of the very large chinchilla ranches.

The first sale of chinchilla pelts in 1944 came at a time when there was genuine ignorance of the type of pelt that needed to come from the industry. Not only were ranchers unfamiliar with the requirements of the fur trade, but furriers, with little or no experience with chinchilla furs, were uncertain also.

On May 2, 1944 a total of 3,315 pelts was offered at an auction held in New York at the auction rooms of Lampson, Fraser, and Huth. Of the 3,315 pelts consigned to the sale, only about 1,000 were actually sold. Prices at this sale ranged from $51 per pelt to a low of $10 per pelt. The low did not actually reflect the bottom, however, because the sale was stopped by the National Chinchilla Breeders Association, sponsor of the sale, in order to protect purchasers of pelts at higher figures.

Reginald E. Chapman, the son of Mathias F. Chapman (founder), who is undoubtedly one of the outstanding authorities in the chinchilla industry, had the following comments to make on the 1944 sale.

"The best prices were for the good quality, clear to slightly off color; if you can imagine, $51; medium and pale were $40—and this brings up something interesting—from the very first day the pelt was ever marketed—right to this very hour —the dark pelts have taken the lead on price. This was against the thinking of most of us in the chinchilla business. Before that, we thought the pale of pales would bring the better price. At any rate, the prices ranged on down to damaged goods, five to eight dollars. Now when they talk about damaged goods, probably ninety percent of the entire offering was damaged, because I don't believe there was a single animal killed for its pelt. I don't think anybody at that time knew how to identify when a live chinchilla's pelt was in prime condition for pelting. We didn't recognize these things in those days. And the quality—this, of course, is a guess, but it is my honest opinion that out of the 3,315 pelts at that offering—I doubt that there were over 15 skins that would sell on today's market. It is amazing to me that the trade was nice enough to bid on them at all."

It would appear that during this period chinchilla pelts were in as great demand as they are today.

Prior to the sale, the National Chinchilla Breeders Association had fostered a small promotional campaign directed to the fur

REGINALD E. CHAPMAN

Reginald E. Chapman, son of Mathias F. Chapman. After his father's untimely death he took over the endless problems and responsibilities of one of the world's greatest conservation projects.

These pelts were photographed in the 30's. The pelts were stretched into a rounded shape, which is not accepted today.

Opposite page: Results of attempts in early day fur dressing. It was not uncommon to have seventy percent or more of the pelts ruined.

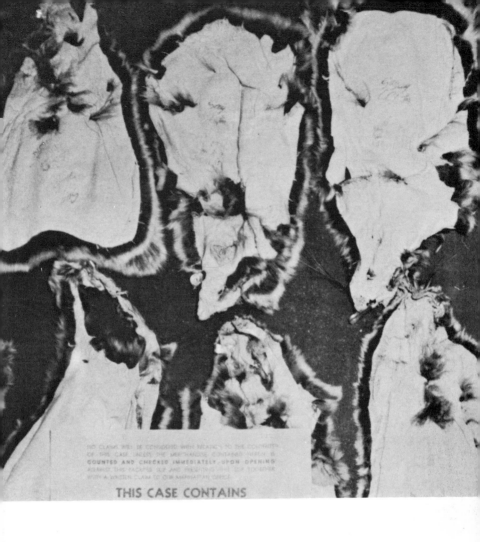

THIS CASE CONTAINS

industry alone. It was a case history, according to the organization's records, in what not to do. Later campaigns by National Chinchilla Breeders Association under the name Empress were directed to the consumer. Although later sales were not always successful, there was, because of consumer interest, a more healthy attitude on the part of fur buyers.

Another important lesson learned in the early sale was the need for proper pelting and fur dressing techniques. Many of the pelts were stained and unprimed, and some of the good pelts had been damaged by improper pelting, handling, dressing, and storage.

In many ways this first sale was a disaster for the industry, but in other ways it keyed the industry for a modern future. While it discouraged many of the ranchers who had survived the lack of interest during the war years, it conditioned those who decided to "tough it out" for the future years. The major trend running through the industry for the next decade was to get ready for the fur market, although there was considerable sentiment on the part of some ranchers that they preferred to raise stock for breeding. Many ranchers hoped to let others go through the process of pelting for an uncertain market.

The first chinchilla association was National Chinchilla Breeders Association. Later an additional association—Farmers Chinchilla Cooperative of America—absorbed the sales responsibilities of National Chinchilla Breeders Association. Still later both were replaced by Empress Chinchilla Breeders Cooperative. There were other chinchilla associations formed which were not related, but for various reasons they existed for just a short time.

In March of 1961 a more vigorous organization was formed in New York, United Chinchilla Associates, Inc.

There was considerable preparation for the Empress pelt sale of 1954. There was a full scale advertising and publicity campaign aimed at the potential customer and at retailers, as well as the fur industry. Farmers Chinchilla Cooperative of America retained the Leber & Katz advertising agency of New York to direct the advertising campaign aimed at introducing chinchilla fur to the consumer. Rosemary Sheehan was retained to handle public relations.

The New York Auction Co. was selected for the sale. The sale, which generated genuine excitement in the chinchilla industry and among furriers, was held June 21, 1954. Approximately 11,000 pelts were consigned to the sale. In the sale about 2,500 pelts were sold before the Farmers Chinchilla Cooperative of America halted the sale, as prices began to fall very low. This again was an action protecting not only the producer, but also the purchasers, at what the organization believed to be satisfactory prices which were limited by the amount of better pelts offered at the sale.

The highest price paid at this sale was by Leo Ritter, a furrier, who said paid $175 per skin for a group of 20 skins. The drop-off in price was swift, however, with the lowest price in the sale dropping to $12. The overall average price paid in the sale was $36.

The sale was a graphic illustration of what many of those prominent in the industry had been preaching: good quality and color. This is what the furriers bought. Another effect of the sale was to help end many of the outrageous predictions as to the expected prices for chinchilla pelts.

In the 60's, United Chinchilla Association and Empress Chinchilla Breeders Cooperative receipts showed a few sales above $50, which, of course, were for top quality pelts. Better quality pelts brought around $30. However, the industry average was less than $20. This is taking into account pelts that brought as little as $5.

The time when any organization has been able to control the price of breeding stock has long passed. The industry has gradually become totally aware that the marketing of furs had to be its main goal.

With the exception of a few unscrupulous marketing organizations, most ranchers believe they will sell only a small percentage of their stock for breeding purposes. There has been some interest in selling animals for laboratory work, but much cheaper animals exist for this purpose, and there is presently no indication that laboratories are going to be willing to pay a higher price for chinchillas on an extensive basis. However, some larger ranchers have donated animals for research.

The emphasis has come to be on improving the quality of chinchillas being raised in terms of color and quality. There has, of course, been developed another almost separate industry within the chinchilla ranching business in the development of mutations—charcoals, beige, blacks, and rose.

The important product, however, continues to be the blue-gray pelt, which has attracted considerable consumer approval.

Chapter IV THE CHINCHILLA

The chinchilla, like other domestic livestock, varies in quality in terms of fur, conformation and health. The general appearance of the animal stems from types, and also from the selective breeding taking place since the beginning of the chinchilla industry.

There are three basic types of chinchillas represented in the population of ranch chinchillas that have relatively few ancestors. All are members of the animal family chinchillidae.

By far the largest numbers of chinchillas on ranches are the Lanigera type, (Chinchilla Lanigera bennetti), or crossbreeds with Lanigera blood. The two other types of chinchilla are the Brevicaudata and the Costina.

The Lanigera has a body from 12 to 14 inches in length with a four to five inch bushy tail. Average animal weight is from 16 to 24 ounces, although there have been exceptional instances where females of up to three pounds (Big Bertha, on a California ranch, weighed in at this top figure in 1967) have been recorded.

The female is generally larger and more aggressive than the male. Nocturnal in habit, the chinchilla has relatively poor daytime sight, and makes extensive use of its stiff whiskers that run up to five inches in length, and can often be used as feelers during its nocturnal activities.

The gestation period of the Lanigera is 111 days, and the Brevicaudata produces young in 128 days. Male crossbreeds of the Lanigera-Brevicaudata are sterile, but females usually are not.

The chinchilla has tiny fingernails rather than claws. The squirrel and the chinchilla have in common one strong characteristic—sitting upright on the rump and holding chunks of food in the paws.

The Brevicaudata has longer hair than the Lanigera, making it appear larger; but is not as clear in color. It is also blockier with shorter extremities, including the tail and legs. The blockier conformation and larger size, as well as the Brevicaudata's extreme fur density have been the reasons for its introduction into the Lanigera strain. It is also by temperament less lively than the Lanigera.

There are several ranches (called farms) in Chile and Argentina that have pure bred Brevicaudatas only, and there is an effort to breed better colored pure bred Brevicaudatas, as well as more productive animals. So far these efforts have been rather limited in success, but there are still possibilities along this line. Some chinchilla people feel that more could be done with pure bred Brevicaudatas than with cross breeding.

More common throughout areas of Chile, Argentina, Peru, and Bolivia are the chinchilla rats and mice. Altiplano Chinchilla Mice (Chinchillula sahamae) thrive at elevations of 4,000 to 5,000 meters. The length of the head and body is from 6 to 7 inches, and the length of the tail is about 4 inches. In many aspects he resembles the chinchilla as we know him.

Chinchilla Rat (Abrocma bennetti) lives at the same approximate altitudes as the chinchilla mice under basic conditions, but he is slightly larger and has stronger resemblance to the chinchilla.

Their pelts are often sold to gullible travelers as genuine chinchilla pelts. However, their pelts are of little value.

In fact, one of the leading chinchilla fur dressers, Lloyd Sullivan, of Oakhurst, California received a shipment of chinchilla rat pelts with instructions to pick out the better pelts and dress them, undoubtedly intending them to be made into a garment.

LANIGERA

There are three different breeds of chinchillas raised for fur: the Lanigera, Brevicaudata, and the Costina. The Lanigera produces the most desirable fur. The Costina and Brevicaudata have some good qualities and have been cross bred with the Lanigera. The chinchilla industry, by and large, uses the Lanigera type.

COSTINA

BREVICAUDATA

CHINCHILLA RAT

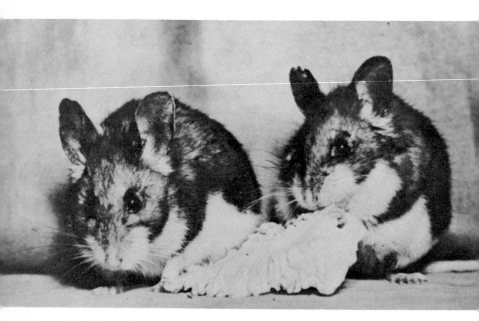

CHINCHILLA MICE

Commonly found in parts of Argentina, Bolivia, Chile, and Peru are the chinchilla rats and chinchilla mice. In many respects they resemble ranch raised chinchillas. In some of these South American countries the natives sell the pelts from chinchilla rats and mice to gullible travelers.

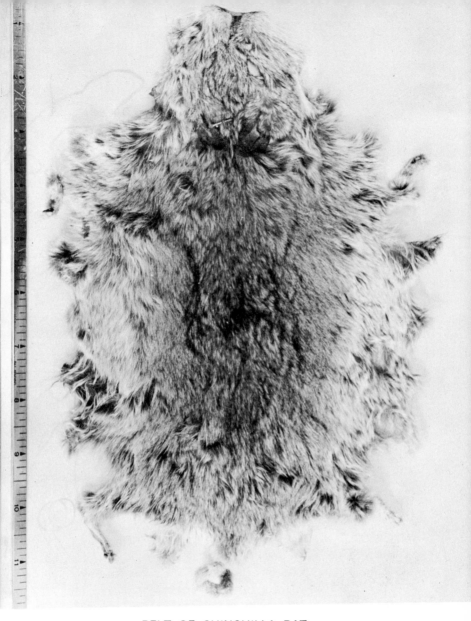

PELT OF CHINCHILLA RAT

In mid 1968, Sullivan Fur Dressing received a shipment of pelts
with instructions to pick out the better pelts and dress them. A
note was attached to one of the pelts: "This pelt was purchased in
South America. The buyer was told it was chinchilla. I believe it
to be chinchilla rat. Do you know?" (Signed) L. S. The pelt shown
is one of the pelts in the shipment.

Another characteristic chinchilla difference includes a large Roman nose on the Brevicaudata. The deepset appearance of the eyes is due to the greater fur growth (or depth) on the head. It originated at higher elevations than the Lanigera.

The third type of chinchilla is the Costina, which is smaller than the Lanigera and has racier lines. It is generally more thinly furred, although its fur has an excellent resilience and is of a fine, silky texture. Its introduction into the Lanigera strain has produced an improved fur. It is sometimes bred into the Lanigera strain in an effort to reduce coarseness and woolliness of fur.

Because the chinchilla is produced for its pelt, the color and quality of the fur are prime considerations, in addition to size.

The chinchilla's fur has often been compared by furriers to the silky gossamer of the spider's web, and not without reason.

Barring mutations, which have become a separate industry within themselves in the chinchilla industry, the chinchilla's fur should be clear gray with a bluish cast.

Chinchilla fur should be observed under proper lighting conditions. Accepted lighting is: daylight fluorescent tube, daylight bulbs, full spectrum lamps, or north light in the shade on a clear day.

Before a solid industry could be built, it was obvious that standards had to be established to determine what were quality animals.

Willard George, a furrier from Hollywood, California developed a grading system in the late 1930's. This grading system is still used today and is the forerunner of other grading methods.

The basic requirements determining the quality of a chinchilla are: clearness of color, undercoat, veiling, finish, density, texture, and conformation.

There are three colored areas in chinchilla fur—the tip or veiling; the bar; and the undercolor which runs from the bar down to or near the roots—however, there are only two colors in a chinchilla. The color of the fur structure itself, and the color of the pigment within it.

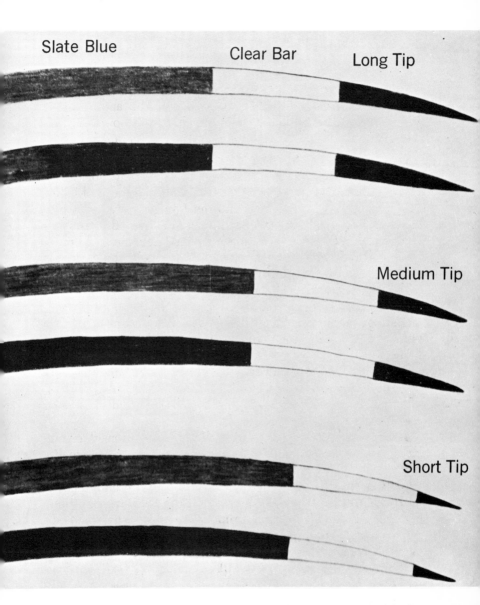

Slate Blue   Clear Bar   Long Tip

Medium Tip

Short Tip

There are three colored areas in chinchilla fur. Next to the skin is the undercoat. Above that is a white bar, ⅛" to ⅜" wide. Above the bar is the tip, black in color. The longer the tip, the darker the animal will appear.

CHINCHILLA STANDARD
Judging Sheet

A Service of
Chinchilla Advanced Standard Scoring System
P.O. Box 824 • OAKLAND 4, CALIFORNIA

Record Sheet N⁰ **44951**

Brand _____   Ranch _____
No. _____   Address _____
City _____   State _____   Judge _____
(VOID UNLESS SIGNED BY AUTHORIZED JUDGE)
Date Judged _____

CLASS	BASIC COLOR FACTORS										BASIC FINISH FACTORS								BASIC FUR FACTORS									BODY FACTORS
	Clearness of Surface Color	BAR							Under Color	Understrip	VEILING						Finish	Structure	QUANTITY OF FUR							Texture	Size
		Clearness of Color			Sharpness	Width of Bar					Smoothness			Coverage					Density			Guard Hair	Depth				
☐ Dark		Shoulders	Body	Hips		Shoulders	Body	Hips			Shoulders	Body	Hips	Shoulders	Body	Hips			Shoulders	Body	Hips		Shoulders	Body	Hips		
☐ Medium																											
☐ Pale																											
Ideal																											
Advanced																											
Standard Plus																											
Standard																											
Average	A	A	A	A	A	A	A	A	A	A	A	A	A	A	A	A	A	A	A	A	A	A	A	A	A	A	A
Inferior	B	B	B	B	B	B	B	B	B	B	B	B	B	B	B	B	B	B	B	B	B	B	B	B	B	B	B

Most grading systems contain the same basic information. Some grading systems go into more detail than others. It must be remembered that when an animal is graded, the grade is in the "eye of the beholder."

The bar is found in all chinchillas. It is an unpigmented portion of each hair. This is why chinchilla fur cannot be imitated. When the tip, or veiling, is very short, the animal will tend to look pale. If it is longer, it will appear to be medium; if it is much longer it will appear to be a very dark animal.

The surface structure of the hair is called cuticle; the next structure is called cortex, and in the center is the medulla—or the middle part. The medulla is a rather spongy part of the hair, and this part runs from the root structure to the bottom of the bar. It discontinues at the underside of the bar. There is usually pigmentation from the root of the hair to the bottom of the bar. Then pigmentation is not found in the clearest colored hairs in the bar, but starts again at the very tip and is called veiling.

BLEND-TRAST FUR GRADING SYSTEM

BLUE RIVER, OREGON 97413   (A.C. 503) 822-3262, 896-3212

Chinchilla
CHARCOAL BLACK MUTATION

B 1062

CLASS _____

GRADE _____ A′ ___ A

COLOR DIV. { LIGHT ☐   MEDIUM ☐   DARK ☐ }

YNG AD ☐   ADULT ☐   YOUNG ☐

DATE _____ 19___

L.E. _____ R.E. _____

GRADER _____
(Not official unless signed)

MALE ☐   FEMALE ☐

FUNDAMENTAL FUR QUALITIES

CLARITY			DENSITY		VEILING PATTERN		VEILING COVERAGE	
Sharp Clear	☐	A′	Very Dense	A′	No Pattern	A′	Dense	A′
Off Clear Slightly Cast	☐	A	Dense Above Average ☐	A	Evenly Patterned	A	Heavy	A
Tinged	Light ☐ Heavy ☐	B	Average Below Average ☐	B	Whorls, Spirals, Waves Variegated ☐	B	Diffused	B
	Brown ☐ Yellow ☐	C	Thin	C	Mottled	C	Thin	C

COMPLEMENTARY FUR QUALITIES

OVERALL COLOR			FUR STRENGTH		TEXTURE		VEILING EXTENT	
Clear	Blue ☐ Gray ☐	A′	Strong	A′	Smooth	A′	Complete	A′
Off Clear Blue Off Clear Gray	☐	A	Firm Above Average	A	Fine	A	Extensive	A
Cast Blue Cast Gray	☐	B	Average Below Average ☐	B	Open Textured Coarse ☐	B	Above Average Average ☐	B
Brown or Yellow		C	Weak	C	Uneven Wooly ☐	C	Scanty	C

SECONDARY FUR QUALITIES

CHARACTER			EVENNESS OF FUR LENGTH		BAR COLOR		SIZE	
Vivid		A′	Even Length	A′	Clear	A′	Extra Large	A′
Striking		A	Slightly Varied	A	Shaded	A	Large	A
Vague		B	Varied	B	Cast	B	Average	B
Dull ☐ Tinged ☐	Colorless ☐	C	Abnormally Varied	C	Tinged	C	Small	C
UNDERCOLOR			BAR LENGTH		BELLY STRIP EXTENT		CONFORMATION	
Clear	Blue ☐ Black ☐	A′	Uniform	A′	Narrow	A′	Parallel	A′
Clear Slate Blue		A	Slightly Varied	A	Limited	A	Symmetrical	A
Light Gray		B	Varied	B	Broad	B	Tapering	B
Pallid		C	Penetrated	C	Indented	C	Wedged	C

CONDITION: Prime ☐   Near-Prime ☐   Overprime ☐   Rough ☐   Spot Chewed ☐   New Fur ☐   Baby Fur ☐   Pen Stain ☐

The BLEND-TRAST FUR GRADING SYSTEM enjoys world-wide official recognition by national governments and breeder associations. It is the only system so recognized.

© Copyrighted 1967 under International Convention

Transferred _____ Date _____

Owner _____
Address _____
City _____
State or Political Subdivision _____
Country _____

New Owner _____
Address _____
City _____
State or Political Subdivision _____
Country _____

REGISTRY and CERTIFICATION

It is certified that this grade sheet was prepared by the certifying association directly from a duplicate of the original grading.

Animal No. _____   Class _____ is hereby registered to _____ in the permanent archives.

Owner _____

Organization _____   Signed _____

Official Position _____

SPECIMEN

The best type of animal is shaded from its darkest color in the center of the back outward. The underside of the animal is generally nearly white. The best animals show very little of this white when upright. The higher it comes up on the sides of the animal, the less desirable it is.

It can be noted that the ideal conformation and color combination are the blocky individuals with pelts of top fur characteristics. The goal in contemporary breeding is toward this type of animal.

Given this ideal, however, the aim of the chinchilla rancher, as with livestock growers, is to obtain a top quality breeding herd.

There is a sound, underlying principle of animal husbandry at work in this trend. A good male can sire far more offspring, and it is unnecessary to maintain a large number of mediocre or second rate males. It makes space more productive if it can be devoted to breeding females, a few top quality males, and priming animals being prepared for pelting.

It should be remembered that because of the few animals available in the early days of the industry, all animals, except those involved in accidents or attacked by illness, were saved to increase numbers.

Also, because there were no fur standards originally, there was little direction in early breeding programs in general. Only in recent years has there been some progress toward an understanding of the type of animal to which ranchers might point.

There are several sources in practically every area for obtaining animals. Some of these sources have educational programs combined with their sales. Persons considering these programs however, should consider how big a premium they are willing to pay for animals, when much of the price must of necessity support the marketing organization and its educational and counseling facilities.

There are ranchers that supply customers directly, and many of them offer "on the ranch training" at no apparent additional cost.

There are several publications in the field that list breeders, and many local newspapers carry advertisements of ranchers who sell breeding stock.

Persons considering chinchilla ranching should be skeptical of sure-fire claims for income or animal sales. Also, the prospective chinchilla rancher should see as many animals as possible at various ranches before entering this industry. One good way is to attend field days and judging competitions, or visit farms. By observing the grading of animals in these events, persons unfamiliar with chinchillas can gain knowledge about the types of animals desired.

As in every market, the price of breeding stock will depend upon quality and availability. It should be a primary consideration of anyone entering the field to balance the price paid for animals against the investment in terms of building, equipment, housing, feed, and labor costs. Bargain basement animals, as in other areas of livestock raising, probably will not provide returns sufficient to cover costs.

Most chinchilla ranches welcome visitors at certain times, and there is a genuine spirit of good will among ranchers in exchanging information. It is always desirable to write or phone a ranch to make sure a visit is convenient and welcomed.

The variety of prices paid for pelts on current fur markets makes any firm pricing of chinchilla breeding stock more difficult than it will be in the future, when the market is larger and its imbalances corrected by larger numbers.

Rule of thumb often suggests that a breeding female may be worth several times its own pelt value. A male chinchilla may be priced similarly, although just as a good bull is priced considerably higher than common breeding stock, a herd improvement male is likely to be expensive.

Another formula is to consider a breeding female to be worth its own value as a pelt, plus the value of pelts its offspring will produce in a single year. Either way a female can be expected to be worth three or four times her own pelt value, and in some cases, even more. The difficult question, of course, is to determine how valuable the pelt of the female would be.

Prices in the fur market vary to extremes because of the quality of a pelt, which is determined not only by its natural value, but also by the way it has been treated.

Chapter V   HOUSING

Chinchilla ranching in the world today ranges from South American countries to North American countries; Africa, Great Britain, Europe, and USSR.

There are small operations in basements, spare rooms, garages, and converted trailers. There are large ranches with four decades of history and thousands of animals.

In this total picture it is easy to see chinchilla ranching is as varied as the constitution of the animal makes possible. It wouldn't be possible or desirable to detail every possible variation of chinchilla ranching.

There are basic environmental factors necessary, however, in every chinchilla ranching operation. It is the intention of this book to describe the desirable environments for chinchilla ranching, and then show some examples of various types of housing being used.

One of the major causative factors in the variety of chinchilla housing situations has been the adaptability of the animal and the fact that it is virtually odorless, and the problems of sanitation are not great. Ease of care, making possible many part time ranching careers, has been another factor.

Most persons entering the field utilize some already existing space that with some modification can be made useable. Also, many new ranchers will want to care for a small number of animals until they become familiar with handling, and are able to judge quality more surely.

Today's practice is largely directed toward the polygamous method as opposed to raising the animals in pairs.

This means space must permit the grouping of cages. In general, the tendency on most ranches is to have banked groups of wire cages from one to five high.

There are two schools of thought on proper housing conditions. Some ranchers find that their animals thrive in basements and buildings without any windows. Others find high rate of reproduction and good health in their animals housed in dwellings with large windows and lots of fresh air. Both philosophies work well, and it would appear that the individual rancher should determine which method is most practical for his needs.

As in most other aspects of chinchilla ranching, stability is an important factor. Moves tend to make chinchillas uneasy, because of sudden changes in light pattern and noise levels. To produce stability, some ranches have used steady music of a restful type to "screen" outside noises.

Temperature control is nearly essential in terms of both heating and cooling. Although different ranchers may have different optimum temperatures, breeding herds should be maintained in environments with temperatures within the range of 65 to 75 degrees, and there is considerable indication that temperatures of about 68 degrees are the most desirable.

Higher temperatures can kill chinchillas if maintained over any extensive period. Anything over 85 degrees may be lethal, if maintained for extended periods, and some ranches have installed alarm systems to react if temperatures rise to this point. This also could serve as a fire alarm.

By contrast, temperatures below 60 degrees, down to perhaps 35 degrees, will not harm the general herd; but infants, unless protected by heated nest boxes at the lower temperatures, will very often die.

There has been a great deal of interest in cool rooms for animals being primed for pelting. The increased value of furs obtained in this way must be balanced against the cost of building and maintaining such a facility. It is generally believed this type of facility may become economically feasible when ranch population exceeds 1,000 animals.

Opposite page. Reginald E. Chapman poses in front of common type of chinchilla housing used in the early 1930's to the 1940's. The cages were about six feet wide, eight feet long, and eight feet high.

Bottom Photograph. Inside view. Note the nest boxes on the outside of the large cages. The nest boxes appear to be larger than many cages used today.

This page: A popular cage used in the 1950's. Size of cage was about 30 in. wide, 24 in. long, 16 in. high, with an exercise wheel on the side of the cage. Today, chinchillas are being raised successfully in cages twelve inches wide, eighteen inches long, and twelve inches high.

A second consideration is humidity. This should be kept below 70 percent; the lower, the better. Damper environments cause numerous problems, and where hay is fed, can almost always be expected to induce mold. Sanitation becomes a greater problem as well.

Control of heat, moisture, and noise are all important in the total environment. There are other vital aspects in chinchilla housing. Cages, feeding dishes, the watering system, and dust bath facilities should all be designed and maintained with stress on sanitation and convenience in maintaining clean conditions. Also, because the fur is the product, all housing should be designed and built with an emphasis on safety.

There are two schools of thought on chinchilla raising conditions. One school holds that a controlled environment can be engineered for any, or almost any, climate. The other extreme holds than one would do best to find a climate fully suited.

All sharp edges should be avoided, particularly in priming cages. Injury can be as dangerous a threat as disease. Nothing is sadder than the necessity of pelting as a casualty a top breeding animal that might have had a useful life span of five years in the herd.

Wire cages, either in whole or at least in part, have become standard in the industry in recent years. They have the virtue of ease of maintenance, and many ranches have moved in the direction of total wire cages that are "self cleaning" with wire mesh bottoms. Where wood is used, such as dividers, it is important that there be no exposed edges or corners on which the animals can gnaw.

It is also important, particularly in priming cages, to avoid wood in any area where it can retain urine, water and feed, that can stain the fur.

An important consideration should be cages that do not permit easy escape, although every experienced rancher will keep a net handy, and doors closed when animals are being handled, and when he first enters the area.

Most ranchers have larger doors on priming cages to prevent accidental injury to animals and their pelts. It must be remembered that the animal, when frightened, can slip fur, just as the porcupine lets go of its quills.

Although there are no ultimate sizes in cages, the trend has been toward smaller sizes. Certainly over the last 20 years the cage size has virtually halved.

On modern ranches, there are variations in cage sizes that range from 20 inches wide by 24 inches long by 15 inches high, to those 7 inches wide by 15 inches long by 15 inches high. The latter size is more commonly used for priming.

The cage sizes include the male's run in the polygamous breeding complex, although in some instances the run has been extended out of the cage in the back.

Most cage constructions are in multiple units of from 3 to 8 to permit handling of a cage block and its removal, without disturbing the entire bank of cages. Many cages are wall hung, but others are placed on racks.

Cage construction allows for a pellet feeder, a hay feeder, and a water bottle. Also, in many modern cages, provision is made for the dust bath; either in each cage or common to each two cages. Accompanying photographs show the variety of possible cage design.

Because the cost of each space will be a factor in total production costs, every effort is made by ranchers to keep these costs as low as possible. Many ranchers use such salvage materials as tin cans and large bottles for feeders and dust baths.

Most ranchers who build their own cages use jigs to bend the wire. Cages are intended usually to have a life of from 10 to 15 years, which makes building them right initially important.

The jig built cage is uniform, faster, and permits exact estimation to assure use of wire with little or no waste. For the new rancher there is a variety of commercially manufactured cages and complementary equipment. They will naturally cost more than self-manufactured housing and equipment. Some types will however, provide trouble-free operation.

The container for pellets can either be of the dish type, or self-filling variety. It is essential that self-filling types of pellet containers have visibility to the reservoir, however, so that it will be possible to see how rapidly foods are being consumed. The containers need to provide space for about two tablespoons of pellets, but some ranchers use feeders of larger capacity.

Garage converted into a chinchilla unit. Two thirds of the back of the garage is used for housing chinchillas, and the front third is used for a workshop and storage. This type of operation can house approximately 200 breeding females plus males and offspring.

A chinchilla unit which is housed in a specially built room. The room is self-contained with a heater and air conditioner. The same results can be obtained by using a spare room. An area eight feet by ten feet is adequate to start raising chinchillas.

Photograph right: shows how the male's run is built along the side of the cages at approximately a forty-five degree angle. Other types of cages have the male's run built along the back or top of the cages.

41

Chinchillas are being raised successfully in basements. Ranch shown above is a full basement capable of housing 450 breeding females and males. Some advantages of this type of operation are very little, (and often), no building costs; little or no heating and cooling. However, in some areas, there may be a moisture problem, which usually can be solved with a dehumidifier.

Opposite page. Building constructed of wood, with a concrete floor. Cages are stacked three high, making observation easier — compared to cages stacked five or six high. Space between floor and bottom row of cages is boxed in for easier cleaning. This unit houses 300 breeding females.

Climate is an important factor in determining type of building. The ranch shown is located in high mountain country, where sturdy construction is needed. The building is constructed of cement blocks and has a concrete floor. Cages are stacked five high to compensate costs of construction, heating, and air conditioning.

This ranch is located in central California near the ocean. Because of the mild climate, heavy construction is not necessary. This building is wood frame with a metal roof, and a dirt floor. Since building and maintenance costs are low, the cages are in a single row, permitting easy observation of animals.

45

Another container or rack for hay is desirable. New ranchers will want to consider whether they will be feeding any of the dehydrated hay pellets when deciding on a type of construction.

By far the most common type of watering device is the baby bottle with a cap holding a capillary-action tube. The bottle is mounted on the outside of the cage with the tube going into the cage. Most are mounted with springs, which is an easy way of fixing them in place and makes changing easy as well.

There are several types of automatic and semi-automatic watering systems available, operating either tanks that must be filled, to those having direct access to the watering system. Most of these systems use release type tubes at the cage, where the animal nudges the tube with its nose to obtain water. Ranchers report that there is initially a good deal of play with the nozzles, but the novelty soon wears off.

Weekly cleaning of food containers and the cleaning of water bottles as often as they are filled (about every three days) is considered to be a practical schedule. If cage mounted dust baths are used, they can be shoved into the cages as part of the feeding schedule.

Use of commercially prepared dust bath mixes is nearly universal in the industry. The dust bath material is available from chinchilla supply firms and a few livestock supply houses.

A screen that fits the dust bath for sifting out droppings is convenient and necessary for those that are mounted on cages.

The self-cleaning cage with paper under it has become one of the common types of chinchilla housing. Its virtue is ease of cleanup, and also provides the opportunity for easy scrutiny of droppings for early detection of problem conditions.

There are several items of equipment that are necessary under special conditions. Most breeding colonies control the access of females to the male's run with the use of collars. Collars have also been used to prevent fur chewing, particularly in instances where the condition is temporary.

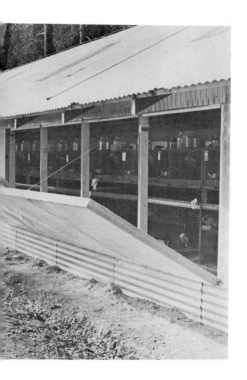

Some ranchers maintain an even temperature in the chinchilla units, while others are strong believers in plenty of fresh air, and will allow the temperature to vary as much as 20° in twenty-four hours. During the winter months the temperature in the chinchilla units will drop to the mid 40's before the heating system will go on. In the summer, the temperature will go into the high 70's before the cooling system will start to operate.

Open shed housing was originated by Mathias F. Chapman. Open shed housing is used in many parts of the world, climate permitting. Among the advantages of open shed housing are low construction cost and maintenance, and no heating or air conditioning expense.

Eight and one half inch tile is placed about two feet into the ground. During the summer it will be about eighteen degrees cooler than outside temperature in the den, and about eighteen degrees warmer than outside temperature in the winter months.

The male's run is continuous, running the full length of the cages. This permits the breeding of as many females as the male is capable of servicing. For instance, a virile male may be able to service ten females, while another male can service six females.

There are many different types of feeders. Shown here are those most commonly used.

Top: A self feeder which holds approximately a week's supply of feed.

Center: This type of feeder is very popular with ranchers who feed once a day.

Small tin cans can be used as feeders.

A popular watering system is a one half pint bottle with a glass tube, which operates on the capillary principle. It is held in place with a commercial holder. It can also be placed in a "homemade" holder, made of mesh wire, as shown in the top photograph.

Gravity flow watering system. Water container is placed on top of the cages. A single tube coming out of the container leads to other lines and on into each cage.

Recirculating watering system. Water is pumped up to an overhead pipe to which smaller tubes are attached. Water trickles down from the smaller tubes into the heads, then into a lower pipe which returns the water to a reservoir. The cycle is repeated.

Many different receptacles are used as dusters, ranging from gallon cans to fish bowls. The duster shown here is a gallon jar set inside a tin ring, which adds stability.

Left: Duster mounted on the outside of the cage. A tin slide is used to permit entrance.

Right: Ranchers using larger cages often use a duster that remains in the cage. This type of duster can be opened and closed from the outside of the cage.

In recent years efforts have been made toward automation. The dusters in these cages work on a rotary system. By turning the handle, the dusters rotate to a position permitting the chinchilla access to the duster. The bottom of the cage is made of plastic and is slanted, causing droppings and urine to drain from the cage into a trough.

Dust bath material does not deplete rapidly and may be used many times. However, droppings and other matter should be removed. The dust can be cleaned easily, as shown in the top photograph. Some ranchers have developed more convenient methods, as shown in the bottom photograph.

The photographs on pages 57, 58, and 59 show how to overcome some of the more common problems encountered in building cages. Bending wire: two 2 x 6's are hinged together, an angle iron is fastened to the bottom 2 x 6 which is used for the bending edge. A clamp will hold the wire in place.

A jig should be used to assure uniformity of cages.

Top: shows placing ends and partitions in the jig.

Left: removal of ends and partitions after being nailed in place.

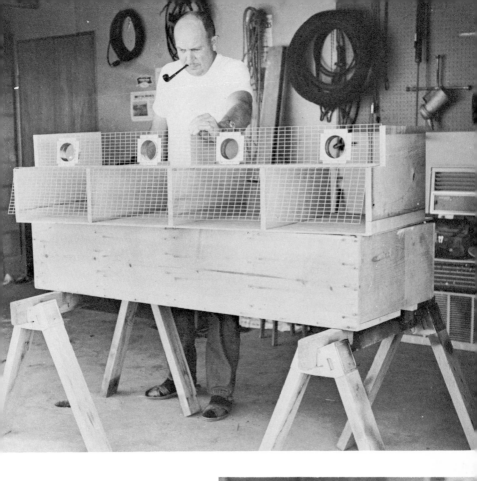

Jig makes a good work bench where space is limited. Sharp edges in completed cages must be filed smooth.

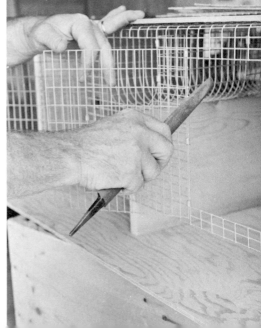

Chapter VI NUTRITION

Good chinchilla stock properly housed forms a basis for sound ranching operations. Added to this foundation must be a desirable diet.

Possibly in no other area of chinchilla ranching is there so much variety of opinion concerning the best practice. Historical development and research indicate this great variety is in part a testament to the hardy characteristics of the chinchilla. They have been known to survive on very unusual diets.

Another important factor is the variety in housing and other environmental conditions. The trend toward the smaller cage has definitely had a relationship in terms of diet.

Good chinchilla ranching practice has moved toward more simple diets. The 1-2-3 diet, having its basic ingredients as pellets, hay, and water, has become the general diet in the industry.

There has been experimentation with other diets, including the single feed diet, utilizing a feed containing the nutriments and benefits of pellet and hay in a combined feed, following the research that led to the one pellet "Wisconsin Diet."

The entire aspect of nutrition, however, should be viewed in terms of stability and consistency. Whatever the values of one particular feeding program over another, changes should be introduced carefully and infrequently.

Ranchers studying the various opportunities for improvement in their feeding program will want to experiment with a small number of animals, and then broaden a desirable feed program to include the whole herd, after it is proven.

Some ranchers will feed two different brands of feed—giving one brand to half of the herd, and another brand to the other half of the herd. The reason for this is that in the event a problem should develop, it would be easier to determine if the difficulty is in the feed. This method would appear to be more practical for larger herds.

The importance of certain types of diet can be best understood in the light of the chinchilla's eating and digestive system.

The chinchilla has 20 teeth. Four of them are incisors; two on the upper jaw and two on the lower. The incisors grow throughout the entire life of the animal. They remain sharp because of constant wear.

The animal has four upper molars and four lower molars. It appears that the molars continue to grow throughout the life of the animal at a lower rate than the incisors.

Autopsies have shown the chinchilla to have a small intestine about four feet long, and a large intestine six feet in length. At the point where the large and small intestine come together is a sack-like organ known as the cecum.

The cecum, in the chinchilla, is larger in proportion to its intestines than in most other animals.

PUMICE STONE BLOCK.

The chinchilla's teeth grow throughout its life span. Many ranchers keep a pumice stone in the cage for the chinchilla to gnaw on, to help prevent its teeth from getting too long. If the teeth should become too long, it may be necessary to clip them, as shown on the opposite page. When clipping the teeth, care should be taken not to shatter them. Large fingernail clippers are often used for this purpose.

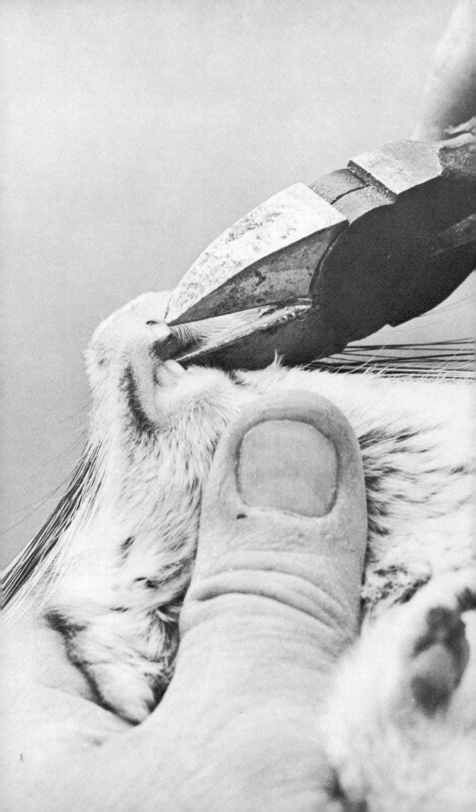

Purpose of the cecum is to break down otherwise indigestible roughage with bacteria. The chinchilla's original environment is undoubtedly the biological origin of its large cecum, where its diet had to be obtained largely from roughage.

Study of the cecum has shown that food passes through it as the result of muscular contractions in the cecum walls, with food passing through at the rate of a complete turnover every six hours, depending on the health and activity of any particular animal.

It is important to note, however, that the food enters and leaves the cecum by the same orifice. This means there is not a complete turnover in the sense that everything going into the cecum leaves it and is replaced by new materials. Material from the cecum probably mixes with material that passes by the cecum.

This fact has importance, when considering the effect of medications or supplements on the chinchilla's digestion.

There has been insufficient controlled and systematic research to definitely determine diet components. Experienced ranchers, however, tend to favor diets which have proven percentages of components, when pellets and hay are considered.

Such a breakdown would be approximately: protein, 18 percent; fat, 4 percent; fiber, 20 percent; nitrogen free extract, 45 percent; and minerals, 6 percent. This dry analysis would account for 90 percent of the diet with moisture and overlapping constituents accounting for another 10 percent.

The daily requirements per pound of body weight are: 1.5 grams of protein; 6.5 grams of carbohydrates; and .25 grams of fat.

As a practical matter the 1-2-3 diet is believed to provide the basic nutritional needs. It appears that chinchillas are to a large degree self-regulating eaters, in that if provided with ample quantities of pellets, or wafers—hay and water—they will select their own diet.

Proper storage of feed is essential. Moldy feed can lead to serious health problems. Hay, pellets, shavings, and other supplies should be stored in dry areas. It is advisable to place all feed and supplies on a raised wood platform as shown.

Open bags of feed should be stored in moisture resistant containers. The smaller rancher finds disposal containers adequate. The larger rancher will often use a more elaborate storage system, as shown on the opposite page. The system used here is a hopper divided into compartments which contain pellets, shavings, dust, and bark. (Bark is shown on page 103).

This generality, however, has to be qualified to the extent that the availability of rich foods, such as seeds (sunflower, for example) or nuts, or excessive amounts of such items as raisins can alter animal appetites within their relatively confined quarters and cause digestive upset, or at the least, an unbalanced diet that does not produce top condition in the animal.

There is a large variety of pellets on the market that have been used by chinchilla ranchers successfully. In the mid-sixties some of the large commercial feed companies provided regular chinchilla pellets on a commercially feasible basis. Ranchers had, for a number of years, previously used rabbit pellets and guinea pig pellets.

The research behind the commercially prepared chinchilla pellet is impressive, and within the bounds of price and availability it is recommended over foods prepared for other animals. Some of the larger ranches have also developed formulas for their own use, and in a few instances are marketing these pellets on a local and national basis.

The question of hay is the thorny one, and this isn't only a pun. The fact is that hay is one of the most difficult purchases for the rancher. It has probably been this factor that has led to some stimulus for the single-pellet diet, hay wafers, and hay cubes.

The basic requirement in the use of hay, however, is that it must be clean, dry, free of dust, weeds, mold, and any trace of rodent droppings; be kept in a dry, well ventilated place where it is protected from contamination by birds and rodents. Equally important, such hay should not come from fields that have been used as pasture or from those treated with insecticides.

Availability of certain types of hay, or their lack, has modified the original contention by many ranchers that only good quality Timothy hay was suitable for feeding. There have been successful uses of alfalfa and combinations of Timothy and alfalfa. There have also been successful uses of other hay types including lima bean, prairie, trefoil, brome, etc.

The difficulty in storing hay has led to a much more frequent use of dehydrated hay in the form of pellets, wafers, and cubes. Ranchers using this form of hay are often happier than with inferior hay. These forms of hay, however, must still come from a dependable source that has assurance against insecticides or other types of contamination.

More than one successful user of hay makes purchases that will last from several months to a year, and controls his own storage carefully. Some ranchers will make a gradual introduction of a new hay crop by adding it fractionally to the diet in increasing amounts until it is the single component. As an example, new hay might be introduced with one-fourth of the hay available to the animals being from the new crop for a week or two, then a half, then three quarters, and eventually a total diet of the new crop. The same procedure is used in changing pellets. This may seem to be an over-cautious approach, but this type of care is characteristic of the successful rancher.

Although there have been some reservations on the part of researchers, there is almost unanimous belief by ranchers that water should be available at all times. There are descriptions of watering systems in the section on housing and equipment.

Water softeners have been known to cause difficulties. The Zeolite method is recommended.

The general rule on water is that it be fit for human consumption, although in instances where there are excessive minerals in the water, or there is extreme treatment with purifiers, chinchillas may have greater difficulty with the water than would people. If well water is used, it is advisable to have it tested.

As in many phases of raising chinchillas, the good rancher is continually looking toward improvement. In the case of diet, this will be equally true, but in a conservative way.

The important factor continues to be "due care." This places an emphasis on keeping the foods (of whatever type) clean in storage, and in clean feeding containers. It is part and parcel in this instance of general ranch sanitation.

While there has been experimentation with timed feeding programs, where animals were exposed to food only for brief periods at certain regular times, the general opinion today is for continual exposure to food.

A regular feeding schedule, however, is considered to be important. This provides an opportunity to see how much the animals are eating in a 24 hour period. Because much of feeding by the chinchillas takes place at night, most ranchers feed in the late afternoon or evening. This is particularly true when the chinchilla rancher has other employment during the day.

The regular feeding schedule permits the rancher to observe behavior. The healthy animal approaches the renewal of food at a regular time with enthusiasm. A lack of enthusiasm for food is one of the crucial warnings that something may be wrong.

While there are instances of chinchillas becoming too fat on some diets, most animals will not overeat. The measure of pellets is determined by experience, but it is generally good practice to provide as much as the animal will eat in the 24-hour period.

A pregnant female will eat more. There are mixed emotions on feeding a supplement to pregnant animals. Many ranchers feel that no supplement is needed if a well balanced diet is fed. There are numerous supplements used by ranchers in addition to the 1-2-3 diet, but in almost every instance it is to correct some problem.

Virtually every other supplement, however, is an adaptation to either a deficiency in the feed being fed, or it is a medical treatment.

Chapter VII HANDLING AND CARE

The selection of animals, their proper housing and feeding, form a foundation for the chinchilla rancher. These essentials, however, must be combined for successful ranch operation.

An ingredient implied, but as important as all three of these, is the operator himself. Perhaps sometime in this era of computers and psychological research, it will be possible to test prospective chinchilla ranchers and tell them if they will be successful.

Because that time hasn't arrived, anyone planning to enter the field will want to reflect on his own resources, not only in terms of time and money, but personality as well.

Probably almost anyone, who is genuinely interested, can become successful in chinchilla ranching, if they are willing to devote the effort and patience required. The successful ranching of chinchillas also depends on methodical operations.

From the time the first animal was domesticated by the cave man, there have been differences in the way these domesticated animals behaved, largely determined by the actions of their owners.

We all know instances where a farmer has livestock that is easily disturbed, and in most instances this can be traced to the way the farmer and his helpers act with the animals.

This same pattern is at work in the chinchilla industry, with added emphasis. It should be remembered that chinchillas have only been domesticated since 1923. In terms of the domestication of most other livestock we raise, this is a very short time. In addition, the chinchilla in its natural environment is timid and nocturnal.

These facts probably account for the chinchilla's need for a quiet, stable environment.

It should be the cardinal rule of everyone involved with the animals that they adopt a calm manner in dealing with chinchillas. The chinchilla will be a friendly animal to the owner who treats him with kindness and care.

A second cardinal rule should surely be awareness. In researching this book, it would be impossible to count the number of times ranchers have said something like, "It's hard to describe how you know something is wrong." Or "I can just tell when something needs to be done, because the animals aren't acting quite right."

Undoubtedly in every situation it would be possible to analyze the behavior of animals and their physical signs, but this "sixth" sense is developed through observation and experience.

This is why someone entering the chinchilla ranching field should start slowly and with a few animals, unless he is an experienced livestock man. There isn't any substitute for experience.

Most successful ranchers recommend that the new rancher start with about eight females, and expand as knowledge and resources are available.

The new rancher will want to adopt a convenient, but regular schedule in caring for his animals. Into this schedule he will want to work feeding, watering, cage and equipment cleaning, caring for sick or injured animals, and along the way, observation of their behavior.

Healthy animals are easier to keep healthy than sick animals are to cure. This philosophy suggests watching the way an animal appears, and the way he reacts to regular feeding.

The most common way to catch and hold a chinchilla is by the tail. When the animal is being held or carried in this manner, it is important that its legs be pointed outward, so that it cannot kick itself free.

When a chinchilla is carried for any distance, the chinchilla should be placed on the arm, thus giving the animal a feeling of security. While holding the animal on the arm its tail should be held firmly so that it can't jump free.

Opposite page: Ideal way to hold a chinchilla when it is being examined or carried.

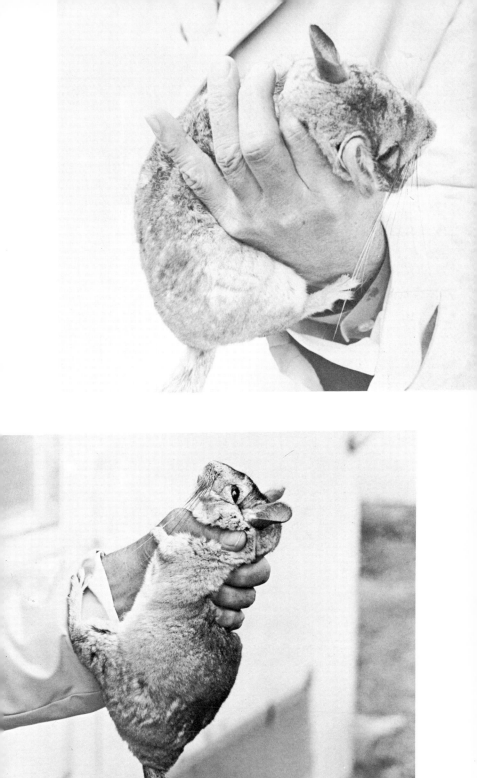

Although special danger signals are discussed in the section on disease, the rancher, as a regular practice, will want to become alert to the general condition of the chinchilla. If the animal fails to approach feed eagerly and happily, it is something to watch.

Another important overall consideration is to handle animals only as much as is necessary for their well being. As in the case of most livestock, too much attention can be as bad as too little. It can overstimulate the animals and keep them from following their natural inclinations.

A typical schedule followed by many ranchers includes a morning inspection for the general health of the animals, to detect any accident or illness, and to discover any new babies. This is also a time to check and make sure all food and watering equipment is in order.

The new rancher will probably be working during the daytime at some other occupation, and will be taking care of his major chores in the early evening. This is the time when food stocks are replenished, water bottles filled, and the paper under cages changed, or shavings in cages changed.

It is a good practice to leave the attention to injured or sick animals until last, unless there is an emergency. This, and the separation of sick animals from the rest of the herd, are part of what should be a regular program of preventive medicine. The rancher will naturally want to wash his hands carefully between handling sick animals, and certainly before handling any animal.

In this connection, chinchillas are hardy and adjust to different surroundings. The animals are, however, easily disturbed. This means that common household pets and children, particularly young children, may not be desirable in the ranching area, until they are taught to behave in a way that will not startle or disturb the animals.

In terms of handling the chinchilla, he is often picked up by his tail and ears, more often by his tail. However, many experienced herdsman do not believe in this method of handling.

They recommend placing the right hand and arm in the cage and catching the animal by the tail with the left hand. Then slip the right hand over the front shoulders, with the thumb underneath the left leg and the rest of the fingers around the chinchilla's neck and body.

Handling chinchillas with this method gives the animals security, and the overall herd is more gentle. This is also a good way to hold a chinchilla during treatment. A little quiet talk seems to reassure them. Gentle handling will produce animals that are not afraid, and as a result they are easier to handle. It is also important to avoid, if possible, any sudden or unusual noise. Many ranchers have discovered that a faulty fan, or air conditioner that makes an unusual noise can cause uneasiness and discomfort.

Some ranchers use relaxing music in their chinchilla areas to screen out sounds that would otherwise startle the animals.

It is worth noting that because the chinchilla can move so rapidly, no opportunity for the chinchilla to go through the cage door should be permitted. Also, when chinchillas are being handled, it is a good idea to have the outside doors to the area closed, and a net available. It is also important not to have storage or debris in the chinchilla area, which will give the animals shelter where they are difficult to reach.

In this connection another important habit is alway keep the doors to the chinchilla area closed when the animals are not under observation, and to check carefully for loose animals when the area is entered.

The desirable qualities of the chinchilla have often been enumerated. They are, to a large degree, odorless; and although timid, they become friendly. It should be noted they seldom bite, particularly if the handler avoids sudden, quick motions, and also places his whole hand in the cage. There have been instances where a single finger poked into a cage has been mistaken for food, and chinchillas do have sharp teeth.

Playing soft music in the chinchilla unit helps screen out harsh, unusual noises that may disturb the animals.

A net with a long handle is the ideal tool for retrieving loose chinchillas.

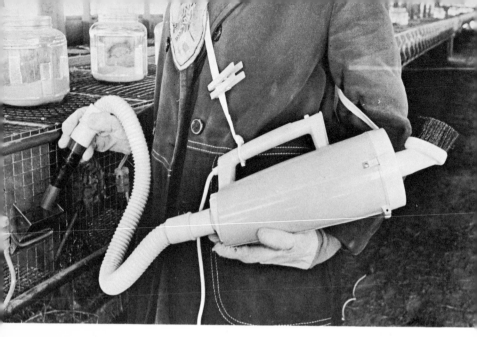

Sediment from feed will set-
tle in the bottom of the feeders, often becoming stale.
Cleaning the feeder with a
vacuum cleaner is a good
practice.

Left: Clothes pin is ideal for
marking cages — indicating
special care is required.

It requires just a few minutes a day to care for a chinchilla. However, as the herd increases more time is required and it may become
necessary to develop time saving devices. It would be impossible
to show in this book all the time saving methods that are being used.
The photographs on the opposite page show how a rancher devised
a method for cleaning shavings from the cages.

Orderly ranch management calls for many different skills and for many different operations. One that cannot be overstressed is sanitation. Many veterinarians are outspoken on the fact that while disease cannot be completely eliminated, the ranchers with the most frequent problems are those whose housekeeping is less than desirable.

Soap and water are essentials around the chinchilla ranch, as they are around the home, where people hope to keep healthy. Eeverything with which the chinchilla comes in contact should be kept clean. This is why it is an advantage to have removable food dishes and watering equipment.

It is almost impossible to say how often pens should be cleaned. Many factors enter into the picture; size of the pen, humidity, ventilation, and temperature. However, a good starting point is once a week.

Another important item to have around the ranch is a good disinfectant to be used on cages where diseased animals have been housed.

Every cage should be completely disinfected or steamed at least once each year—preferably twice a year. Water bottles should be sterilized about every three days, and food dishes at least weekly.

Chapter VIII   BREEDING

Good practice in the chinchilla industry is naturally directed toward maximum reproduction. Whether the goal of the rancher is the sale of breeding stock or pelts for the fur market, it is only possible to have an economically sound operation if reproduction is maximized.

It is this consideration which has focused most activity in the industry on polygamous breeding. As an economic measure it reduces the number of animals required in the breeding herd, and makes better use of top quality males.

Many persons entering the field have done so using pairs. Although pair (monogamous) breeding does not appear to be practical, there are advantages. One, it will acquaint the new rancher with the behavior of males, and two, it gives him the opportunity to select the better males to be used in polygamous breeding.

There is another important consideration. While early in the history of the industry the goal was merely to increase the number of existing animals, this time is past.

The current goal is to produce pelts of high quality fur, since it is obvious that with the large number of ranchers in the industry operating on a large scale, they can't merely continue to sell breeding stock only.

A top quality male can help upgrade a herd, since it can be expected genetically that at least half the babies of a mating between a top quality male and an inferior female will have some of the better qualities of the parents. In practice, this means a continued upgrading of the herd, if there is attention to quality.

The rancher today must be far more ruthless in culling out undesirable animals from his herd. Nothing is more discouraging than to view the line of a relatively inexperienced rancher and find that he is perpetuating the poor quality of inferior animals. There is virtually no opportunity for this rancher to market his animals. Frequently, this has given the chinchilla industry a black eye.

Ranchers have widely differing opinions on the ratio of females to male sires in a polygamous program. There is, however, a general practice of mating from three to eight females with a single male.

It should be remembered that a fine male chinchilla can be as important as a fine bull to the extent he is mated to more females. Efforts to stretch the breeding of a single male with too great a number of females can result in a lower number of offspring, so one must consider this limitation.

The age for first breeding chinchillas is generally from six to nine months. This is the time when the animal has completed most of its growth cycle and is also the time when it is first possible to judge the quality of an animal with a great degree of assurance.

The male is usually introduced to females gradually to assure compatible breeding. Most ranchers place the male in the run of the cages, leaving an empty cage open to give the male access to food and water.

As the male becomes acquainted with the females through the wire, the females' cages are opened, giving the male access to each of them, and eventually to all of them. At this time a female is placed in the empty cage. However, it is advisable to place a female in the empty cage which is compatible with the male.

When introducing a male to a female it is good practice to put a refuge box in the cage. In the event that they should fight, the refuge box will give the chinchilla having the worst of the fight an opportunity for escape. Refuge box shown is built of 1 inch x 6 inch lumber.

Females are collared when polygamous breeding is used. The collar prevents the female from going through the male's jump hole. There are various kinds of collars.

Top photograph on opposite page: A two piece plastic collar.

Bottom: An adjustable collar made of aluminum.

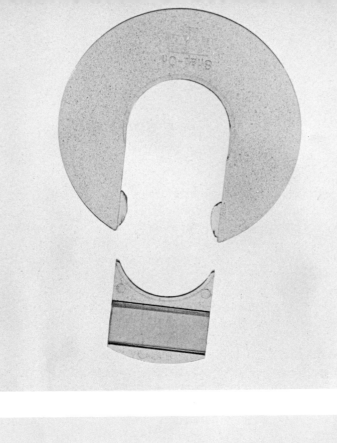

Some ranchers provide up to a week for the male to become compatible with the females, while others use shorter periods of time. Only experience can determine this.

It will be found that the temperament of the animals has a significant bearing on the rapidity of introducing mating animals. Those herds that are generally quiet will accept more casual methods.

Many ranchers provide within their polygamous colonies a refuge box as additional protection. This gives an animal that is having the worst of a fight the opportunity for escape.

Individual animals can breed at virtually any time of the year. The female comes into heat on the average of once every twenty-eight days, although this has been known to vary with individual animals from sixteen to thirty-five days.

While individual animals can theoretically be bred at any time, the experience of most large ranches is that there is a definite pattern within the year.

Breedings generally become frequent in December, and reach a maximum in January and February.

With the gestation period being one hundred and eleven (111) days, litters begin arriving in March, and maximum numbers of babies appear in April and May. Because the animals are easily susceptible to breed-back during the first thirty-six hours after delivery, this also means there is a substantial number of litters appearing in July and August.

August through November is the next peak breeding season. This season pattern can, of course, be affected by variations in climate in various parts of the country.

There are several possible ways to determine pregnancy in females. The females may be weighed at monthly intervals. There is a normal gain of about one ounce for each month of pregnancy in healthy females. This weight increase is most noticeable after sixty days of pregnancy.

CHINCHILLA
GESTATION CHART

The number in the first line represents the day of conception.
Those directly below the expected date of birth (111 days).

Conception / Birth	1	2	3	4	5	6	7	8	9	10	11	12	13	14	15	16	17	18	19	20	21	22	23	24	25	26	27	28	29	30	31	
Jan.	1	2	3	4	5	6	7	8	9	10	11	12	13	14	15	16	17	18	19	20	21	22	23	24	25	26	27	28	29	30	31	
Apr.	21	22	23	24	25	26	27	28	29	30	1	2	3	4	5	6	7	8	9	10	11	12	13	14	15	16	17	18	19	20	21	May
Feb.	1	2	3	4	5	6	7	8	9	10	11	12	13	14	15	16	17	18	19	20	21	22	23	24	25	26	27	28				
May	22	23	24	25	26	27	28	29	30	31	1	2	3	4	5	6	7	8	9	10	11	12	13	14	15	16	17	18				Jun.
Mar.	1	2	3	4	5	6	7	8	9	10	11	12	13	14	15	16	17	18	19	20	21	22	23	24	25	26	27	28	29	30	31	
Jun.	19	20	21	22	23	24	25	26	27	28	29	30	1	2	3	4	5	6	7	8	9	10	11	12	13	14	15	16	17	18	19	July
Apr.	1	2	3	4	5	6	7	8	9	10	11	12	13	14	15	16	17	18	19	20	21	22	23	24	25	26	27	28	29	30		
July	20	21	22	23	24	25	26	27	28	29	30	31	1	2	3	4	5	6	7	8	9	10	11	12	13	14	15	16	17	18		Aug.
May	1	2	3	4	5	6	7	8	9	10	11	12	13	14	15	16	17	18	19	20	21	22	23	24	25	26	27	28	29	30	31	
Aug.	19	20	21	22	23	24	25	26	27	28	29	30	31	1	2	3	4	5	6	7	8	9	10	11	12	13	14	15	16	17	18	Sep.
Jun.	1	2	3	4	5	6	7	8	9	10	11	12	13	14	15	16	17	18	19	20	21	22	23	24	25	26	27	28	29	30		
Sep.	19	20	21	22	23	24	25	26	27	28	29	30	1	2	3	4	5	6	7	8	9	10	11	12	13	14	15	16	17	18		Oct.
July	1	2	3	4	5	6	7	8	9	10	11	12	13	14	15	16	17	18	19	20	21	22	23	24	25	26	27	28	29	30	31	
Oct.	19	20	21	22	23	24	25	26	27	28	29	30	31	1	2	3	4	5	6	7	8	9	10	11	12	13	14	15	16	17	18	Nov.
Aug.	1	2	3	4	5	6	7	8	9	10	11	12	13	14	15	16	17	18	19	20	21	22	23	24	25	26	27	28	29	30	31	
Nov.	19	20	21	22	23	24	25	26	27	28	29	30	1	2	3	4	5	6	7	8	9	10	11	12	13	14	15	16	17	18	19	Dec.
Sep.	1	2	3	4	5	6	7	8	9	10	11	12	13	14	15	16	17	18	19	20	21	22	23	24	25	26	27	28	29	30		
Dec.	20	21	22	23	24	25	26	27	28	29	30	31	1	2	3	4	5	6	7	8	9	10	11	12	13	14	15	16	17	18		Jan.
Oct.	1	2	3	4	5	6	7	8	9	10	11	12	13	14	15	16	17	18	19	20	21	22	23	24	25	26	27	28	29	30	31	
Jan.	19	20	21	22	23	24	25	26	27	28	29	30	31	1	2	3	4	5	6	7	8	9	10	11	12	13	14	15	16	17	18	Feb.
Nov.	1	2	3	4	5	6	7	8	9	10	11	12	13	14	15	16	17	18	19	20	21	22	23	24	25	26	27	28	29	30		
Feb.	19	20	21	22	23	24	25	26	27	28	1	2	3	4	5	6	7	8	9	10	11	12	13	14	15	16	17	18	19	20		Mar.
Dec.	1	2	3	4	5	6	7	8	9	10	11	12	13	14	15	16	17	18	19	20	21	22	23	24	25	26	27	28	29	30	31	
Mar.	21	22	23	24	25	26	27	28	29	30	31	1	2	3	4	5	6	7	8	9	10	11	12	13	14	15	16	17	18	19	20	Apr.

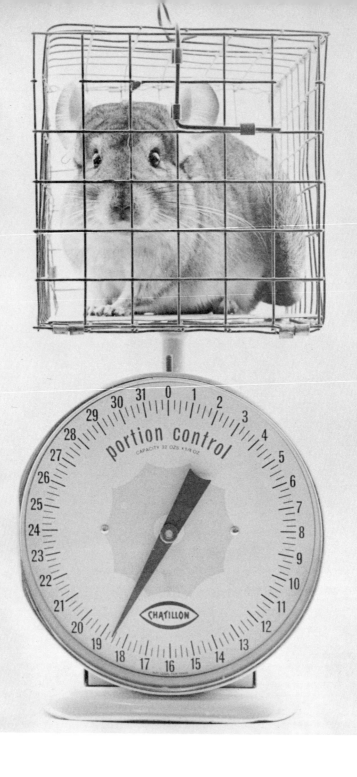

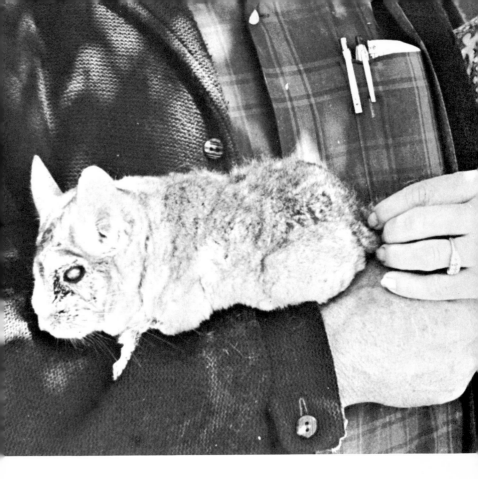

A common question is how long do chinchillas live. Above photograph is of a 23 year old chinchilla. However, it is extremely rare for chinchillas to reach this age. The length of time a chinchilla will be at its maximum productivity is approximately six years. Older animals are less productive.

One of the better methods of checking for pregnancy is weighing the female when it is believed she has conceived; (become pregnant). She will gain about one ounce per month. The most noticeable gains will be apparent in approximately sixty days.

Within sixty days after mating, the nipples of the female will become red and stiff, when normally they are white and soft. About half way through the pregnancy, the female's breasts will also begin to enlarge. Sometimes these changes are very slight, and careful observation is required.

Other signs include a change in appetite pattern. The female will often initially go "off feed" to a degree, and then, in later stages, show an increased appetite.

The signs of a female in heat are often pronounced in the nearby members of the herd, although the mating itself is rarely observed, almost always taking place during the nighttime hours.

Excitement in nearby animals will indicate a female in heat, and often other neighboring males will probably be excited.

Many breeders find that unsuccessful matings between two animals will be successful with a change of mates.

The breeding life of a top quality animal is considered to be about five to six years. There are instances where animals have had longer useful breeding lives. However, in general, the older animal becomes less productive.

One of the most controversial issues in chinchilla ranching is rate of reproduction.

Before any reasonably authoritative figure can be reached, there are a few factors involved that must be taken into consideration.

Newly purchased breeding animals have to become acclimated to their new surroundings, which can vary from one month to several months. However, three months would appear to be a sufficient length of time.

When determining rate of reproduction all the females that are exposed to males must be counted, even if they do not breed.

In discussions with chinchilla ranchers, it has been found that the reproduction rate varies from two to four babies per year per female; two or less is considered poor; three or more is considered good.

The writer's experience and opinion is that 2.5 babies per year per female is a realistic expectation on established ranches.

The only time chinchillas are affected by cold temperatures is at birth. In some chinchilla units it may be necessary to provide heat.

Top photograph: A commercial heater which can be slipped under the pan. Some ranchers use a heating pad.

Right: A home made heater which works well under wire bottom cages.

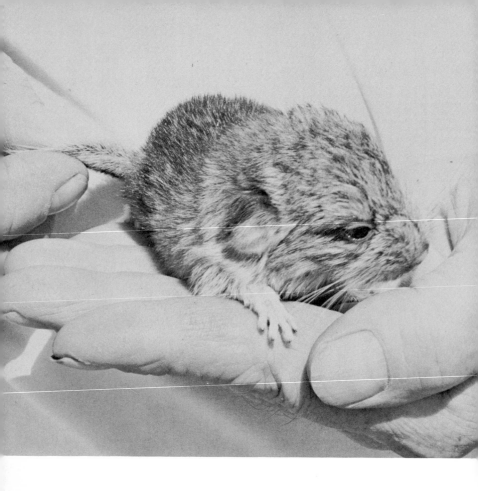

Due to the long gestation period, chinchillas are born with their eyes open, furred, and weigh about one ounce. Within a few hours after birth the new born baby chinchilla is extremely active.

New born chinchillas have sharp fingernails. When nursing, they can scratch the mothers' breasts, which can lead to infection; or the mothers' refusal to permit nursing. It is recommended that babies' fingernails be trimmed. This can be accomplished by dragging the baby's paws over fine sandpaper. Or, the nails can be clipped with a cuticle scissors.

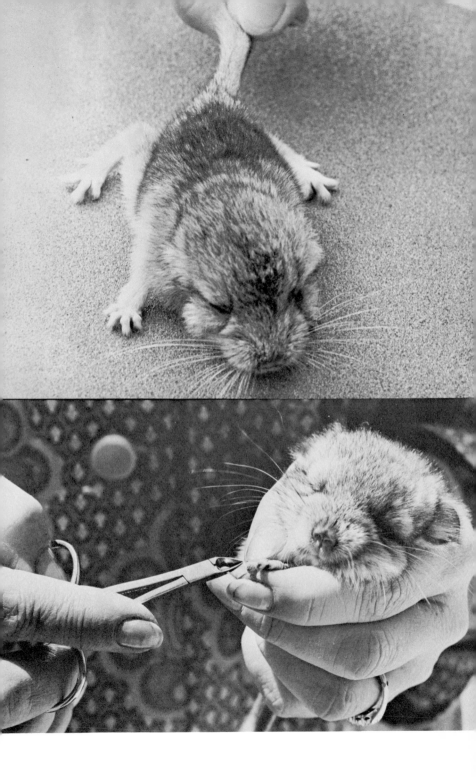

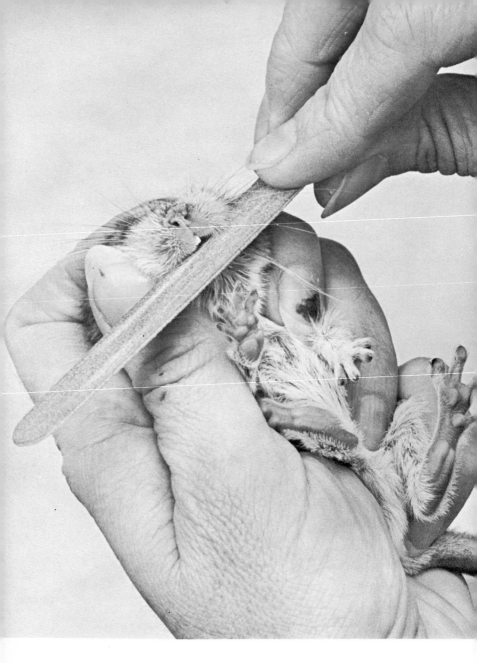

Baby chinchillas are also born with sharp teeth, which can lead to the same problems as sharp fingernails. Their teeth can be filed with an emery board, or a small high speed drill with a fine grinding stone. Either method is effective. The filing or grinding process may have to be repeated about once a week.

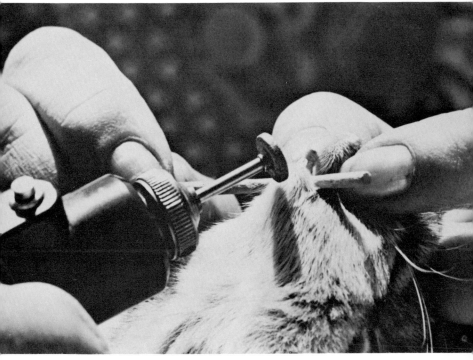

If a well balanced diet is fed, supplementary feeding may not be required. However, if a supplement is needed, a coaster makes a good feeder. It can be placed on the floor of the cage. Some supplements can be put in the pellet feeder.

From time to time it may be necessary to hand feed babies. The most common cause of this is a large litter, and the mother does not have enough milk for all the babies. One accepted formula used in hand feeding is a mixture of two parts canned milk and two parts water. The baby should be held as shown. Just one drop at a time should be placed on the lips. Putting the milk in the baby's mouth can cause choking.

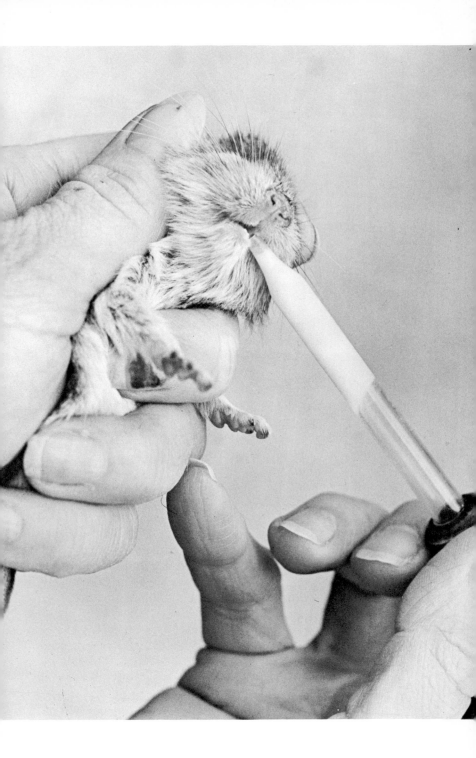

Close observation is extremely essential as the time for littering approaches.

This is virtually the one time when the chinchilla is affected by cold temperatures. Many babies are lost because of the cold temperatures in the first hours after birth.

Ranchers using wire bottom cages will often provide added heat when litters are expected, and some ranchers will put straw in the cages about a week before littering; while others use heat pads or heating elements under the cages.

It should really not be necessary to remove the babies from the mother's cage unless there are problems. There are two conditions which can occur, which suggest close observation.

One is the overproduction of milk which can result in caked breasts. This condition, unfortunately, is most often discovered when babies are injured by the mother.

If this condition is present, breasts should be hand stripped of as much milk as possible. A hot pack should be applied for perhaps fifteen minutes, and the breasts should be treated with a soft lubricant. The condition is most often reflected by inflamed or even cracked nipples. The lubricant will usually keep the babies away from the mother for the necessary time.

If nipples are damaged by the babies, it may be necessary to file down teeth and fingernails of babies that are still nursing. This can be done with an emery board and fine sandpaper. This may have to be repeated in about five days.

The other instance that could create a problem would be where there is a multiple birth and the mother, for some reason, does not provide sufficient milk. The best solution is to give the baby to a foster mother that has either lost her baby, or has only one offspring and plenty of milk.

Close observation is necessary, because some females will not accept a strange baby. Rubbing the baby against the foster mother's fur sometimes helps. Another possibility is to place camphorated oil or perfume on the mother's nose and on the baby's nose and back, so that the different scent is not detected.

Some babies can be saved with hand feeding. This can be done with an eyedropper filled with a formula of canned or whole milk diluted with equal parts of water. This should be fed a drop at a time on the baby's lip, or just inside the mouth. Five or six drops at lukewarm temperature should be given every three hours.

As the baby gets older and gains strength, the amount given at each feeding can be increased and it will not have to be fed as often.

Babies that are hungry and appear to need additional food can also be fed a dry supplement in a small feeder on the floor of the pen. A possible supplement is made with a cup of powdered milk, a third of a cup of Quaker Oats, and a teaspoon of powdered sugar. Pablum or baby mixed cereals may also be used.

Naturally, the mother's milk, or that of a foster mother, is the best food, containing not only nourishment, but also provides some immunities to disease.

Weaning of babies should take place at about forty-five to sixty days, or earlier if the mother is not able to nurse that length of time. Several babies can be placed together in a cage if they are of the same sex. However, it is best to put weanlings in separate cages

If the rancher is using a balanced diet for his herd, there will probably be no need to provide any supplement for the pregnant and nursing mother. The female chinchilla will usually obtain the needed amounts of protein and calcium through additional amounts of the regular diet.

It is best to wean babies in separate cages. However, several babies may be weaned together. Males and females should be separated.

A wood block or bark is often placed in the cage. It helps keep the animal occupied. Woods such as cedar and redwood are toxic.

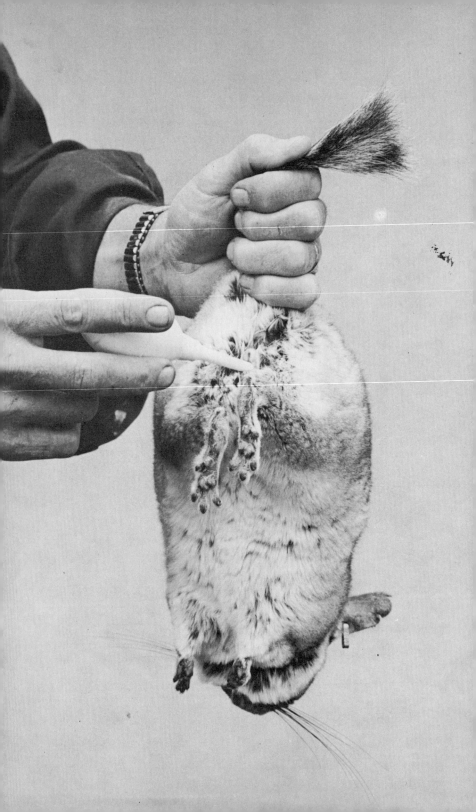

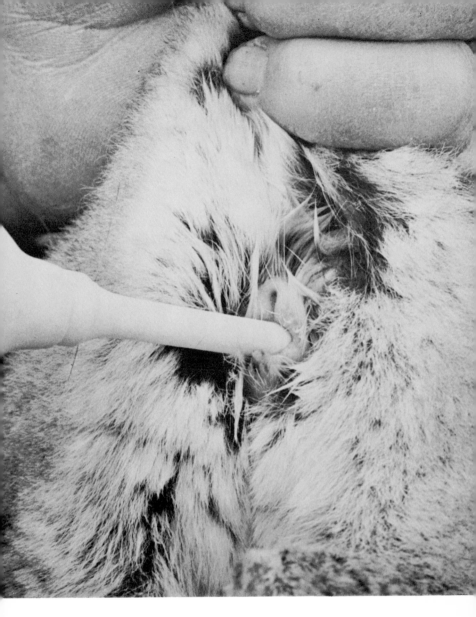

Some ranchers recommend douching chinchillas. Douching helps dissolve and clean out solidified matter that has gathered in the vaginal canal. Females are capable of producing a plug similar to the plug shown on page 199, even though they are not bred. It would appear that a plug in the vaginal tract could prevent the sperm from reaching the reproductive organs. Douching can also help correct this problem. Chinchillas can be douched as shown on pages 104, 105, 106, and 107.

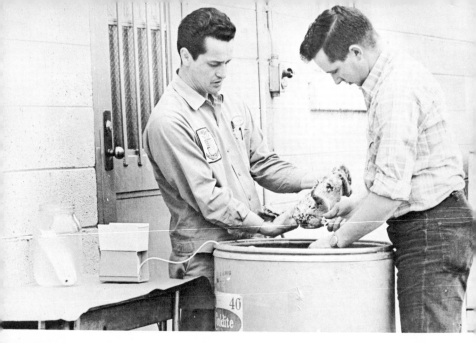

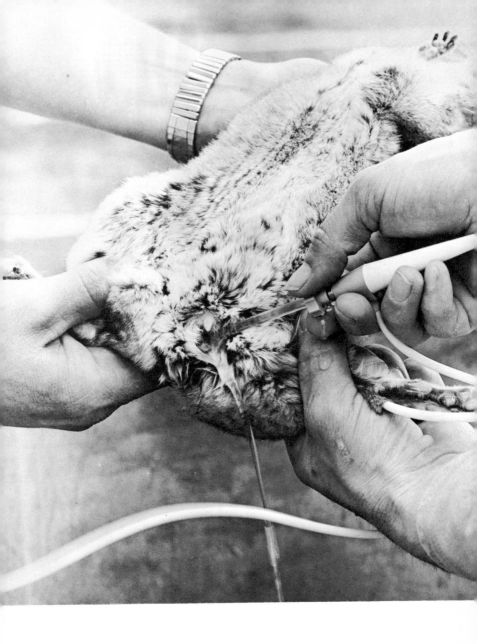

A water pik can be used to douche chinchillas. If a large number of chinchillas are to be douched, a gallon jar can be used as a reservoir. Extreme caution must be used when douching, and a veterinarian should be consulted as to the correct way this should be done.

Chapter IX   PRIMING

Unlike other fur bearing animals, the chinchilla in captivity does not come into prime at certain seasons of the year. This could be because of the artificial environment.

The result is that careful judgment is required in determining when animals have come into prime. It is possible to induce prime through the use of a cold room, or through the use of outdoor or semi-covered priming houses in colder climates.

Experience with cold rooms, where temperatures are maintained in the range from 40 to 60 degrees, indicates that animals can be induced to start new growth in about 60 days, and that it takes another 60 to 90 days to bring the animal into prime.

Priming animals should receive attention equal or superior to any attention given to breeding stock, if a top quality fur is to be obtained. Ordinarily, smaller cages are used to house priming animals. Another feature of the priming cage should be a larger door to prevent any damage to the fur when removing the animal from the cage.

Chinchilla fur grows in from the head backward to the rump, and in a slower manner from the stomach up the sides. An animal is in top prime when the underfur is at its widest and most consistent color, and when there are no more rings of fur growing in. It is possible to examine the skin of a priming animal. Blue areas also indicate the continued growth of fur.

It may be desirable to review the top quality fur characteristics in considering prime. Some ranchers fail to obtain top prices for their furs because they pelt animals just coming into prime, and fail to wait for the full beauty and sparkle that marks the top quality pelt.

The good animal exhibits in prime the desirable pattern with the underfur darkest up on the back, only slightly lighter up on the neck, and only gradually lightening as it moves down the sides or back on the hindquarters.

The bar of white, immediately above the undercolor, should be uniform in the primed animal, as should the black veiling that tops the bar.

Most ranchers either blow into the fur to view extent of priming, or, on large ranches, very often a compressor and air hose are used. It is very important to view the animals being considered for pelting under a good light.

The same type of lighting is used as described on page 28.

This also permits the rancher to view color and note any stains or undesirable pattern. It is well worth the food and space to reprime an animal that has damaged fur, if, by a new cycle, it can be upgraded.

In judging prime, many imperfections will disappear with additional time. Unless an animal has, for example, constitutionally choppy fur, parts, or cowlicks, or other inherited irregularities, additional priming should help remedy this condition. This is also true of priming lines, which appear just before the animal has come into prime, and appear to be bands of varied coloring running across the back and hindquarters.

Many ranchers use specially designed cages for priming animals. The cages are usually smaller, with larger doors than those in the breeding cages. It is easier to catch the animal in a smaller cage, and the larger door helps prevent fur damage when the chinchilla is removed from the cage.

Priming unit shown above is one row, making for easier observation. The photograph on the opposite page shows close up of the priming cage. Note: large door opening on top of the cage.

Priming unit with much smaller cages which are stacked four high, in contrast to that shown on page 110. This is a graphic illustration of different types of equipment and theory used in chinchilla ranching.

Some ranchers use a portable light to check the position of the prime line. Using the light makes observation easier, and less handling of the animal is required.

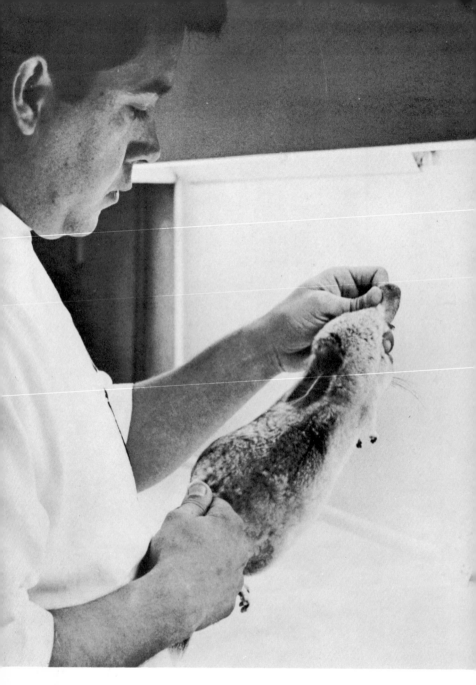

On some of the larger ranches compressed air is often used when checking animals for prime, as shown above. The same results can be obtained by blowing into the fur.

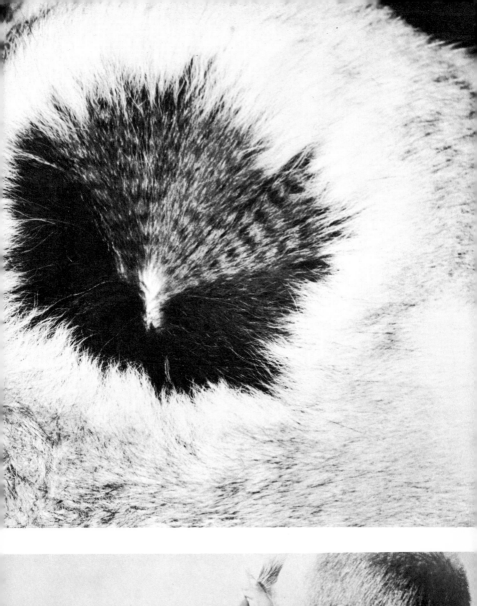

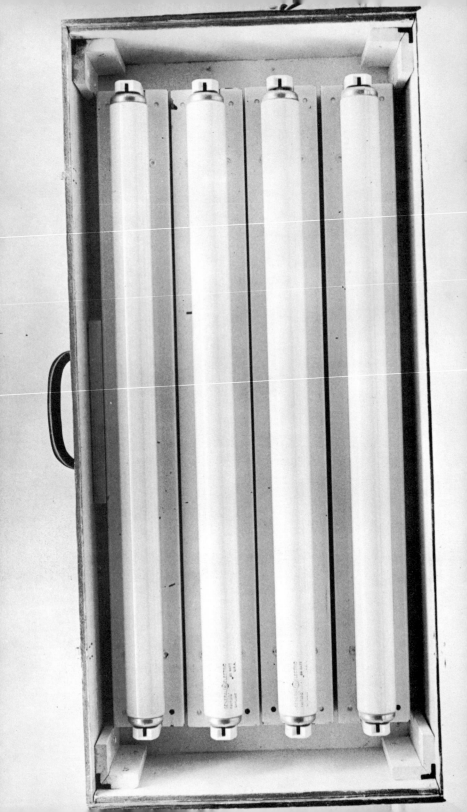

No rancher should be without a grading light and table. Four daylight or full spectrum fluorescent tubes should be used. It is important that the bottom and the sides of the table be painted a neutral color. It is also important that neutral colored clothing or smock be worn when grading chinchillas. For example, if the grader wears a red shirt, it can reflect a red cast on the fur, making accurate grading difficult.

Shipping crates vary in size, design, and material. Cage shown above is the type used in chinchilla shows, and can also be used when moving chinchillas a short distance.

Shipping crate made of wood. It is divided into six compartments, and air openings are covered with 1 inch by 1½ inch wire mesh. The cover slides over the entrance, and it is nailed in place to prevent accidental opening.

Shipping crate made from a cardboard box. The inside of the box is completely lined with ½ inch wire mesh to prevent the chinchilla from gnawing a hole, and possible escape.

119

Animals in full prime show an absence of the double bar rings and a clear color of the underfur.

A good practice is to either keep a record on the pen card, or use a piece of masking tape, similar to that used to note other special conditions, on the cage as a marker to remind the rancher to check prime at specific intervals.

As ranchers gain experience, their ability to judge prime is improved. The new rancher may well want to ask the experienced rancher to check his judgment, and can also profit greatly from several sessions with an experienced rancher who is checking animals for prime, prior to pelting.

At prime, the chinchilla appears at his best in density, color, and consistency of fur.

There are organizations and individuals that offer priming and pelting services at realistic fees. It might be advisable for the new rancher to take advantage of such services if he is unable to have an experienced rancher advise him in this phase of ranching.

Chapter X   PELTING

The whole cycle of the chinchilla ranch is aimed at producing top quality pelts. This makes it doubly important to handle the pelting operation with skill and care to make the previous effort pay off in terms of the top prices that quality pelts bring at the market.

An animal in top prime can still be spoiled with careless or sloppy pelting methods. It is important to develop a method that avoids this.

The first step is to kill the animal to be pelted, and there are several methods, each having its own followers, depending upon experience.

Undoubtedly the most common is electrocution, where a small device, easily built, is employed. A wire cord that can be plugged into a regular socket is run through a switch, and light bulb with the two leads of the wire ending in clips.

A toggle switch is most easily used, since the rancher can leave it on by pressure just as long as necessary to kill the animal. The light bulb is a safety measure, telling the handler when the current is running to the two leads.

Alligator type clips on the two leads make this a very useful method. One is fastened to the chinchilla's ear, and one to the base of the tail. A few seconds is all that is necessary. There are some objections to electrocution. For one thing, microscopic examination of hairs from electrocuted animals show a slight curling, although this is not visible to the naked eye. Animals electrocuted tend to stiffen swiftly, which means they are more difficult to pelt.

Alternatives include the use of gases. One method is to chloroform the animal. It has the virtue of leaving the animal completely relaxed after killing and cooling. A gallon jar may be used as a gas chamber. Cotton saturated in chloroform is put into the jar and the lid screwed on for several minutes to permit the fumes to fill the jar. Then the lid is removed, and the chinchilla, held by the tail, is placed head down into the jar, and the lid replaced. A few minutes will be sufficient to produce death. Some ranchers have manufactured gas chambers that use trays in which the chloroform has been placed in cotton. This has the advantage of permitting the "killing cage" to be set in the gas chamber, and there is less danger the chinchilla will lose fur in struggling, as there may be, if the jar method is not used carefully.

Some ranchers use carbon monoxide by building a chamber to which they can fasten a hose running from a car exhaust. Two cautions are necessary if this method is used. One is to use the killing chamber outside, or in a well ventilated room. The other caution is to screen the end of the nozzle to prevent oil and unexpended gas from staining the fur of the chinchilla. It is necessary to dry the condensation out of the hose after each use.

A third method of killing is to use an injection of a centimeter of alcohol, or a quarter to a half of a cubic centimeter of nembutol directly into the stomach cavity or heart. The only objection to this method is that it requires two persons, and also there is some danger of fur damage if the animal is permitted to struggle.

A few ranchers have been successful using the neck-breaking technique used by many mink ranchers, but the possibility of damaging the chinchilla's fur is sufficiently greater to make it less desirable than almost any of the other methods.

Once killed, the carcass should be permitted to cool. The correct length of cooling time will vary, depending upon temperature. At a temperature of 35 degrees, the animal's body should be cooled for ten to fifteen minutes. At higher temperatures, it will take slightly longer.

Once cooled, the animal is ready for pelting. The operation can be done in several ways, but one of the easiest is that recommended by the United Chinchilla Association.

It requires a razor blade, a knife, a pair of scissors, and an umbrella stave or a stiff wire, as well as pins and a board.

The first step is to cut off the hind legs one half inch above the hocks. Next, the forelegs should be cut, midway between the wrist and elbow.

Then a slit should be made from the tail to the sex organs. The tail should be removed one inch from its base, and the lower one-half inch slitted.

Holding the animal by its whiskers with the thumb and index finger, an umbrella stave can be inserted into a slit in the lower jaw, and pushed through to the organs. Still holding the whiskers, the knife is placed in the groove of the stave, and a slit made back to the organs.

Organs are then clipped off with scissors. The carcass is then worked away from the skin, using the thumb and forefinger of the right hand.

Holding the carcass firmly around the trunk with the right hand, the pelt should be pulled over the leg. It is then possible to work fingers under the neck to separate the pelt from the neck, shoulders, and upper back.

Using the back of the hand to hold out that part of the pelt which has been freed, the carcass can be pulled free to the hips with the right hand. Then, by holding the left hand under the pelt, the carcass can be pulled away with the right hand, over the hind legs.

The pelt can then be removed over the head, clipping the ears, and pulled down as far as the eyes. The pelt can be worked with the forefinger and middle finger over the head, using the knife to free the pelt at the front corner of the eyes.

Once the pelt is freed from the carcass, the tube formed by the hind legs is cut open from the back corner of the pelt. Remaining flesh should then be removed from the pelt.

The drying of chinchilla pelts is currently toward the more modern elongated rectangle, and away from the boxy shape, which has been used in the past. The current goal of the industry is to develop a uniform pelting, which will be more acceptable to furriers, who have often complained about variations in the shape of the chinchilla pelt.

The shaping and pinning of the pelt can be done in the following manner. Two pins can be placed at the head of the pelt, and the pelt brushed backward. It should be lifted occasionally to prevent laymarks.

When laid back the long way, the pelt should not be stretched. Any stain at the base of the pelt should be trimmed. Using a reasonable amount of tension, a pin should be placed in the bottom center of the pelt, and then at each corner.

Additional pins should then be added at the base to spread it slightly, and pins should be inserted at each shoulder. The shoulder width should be less than that of the base.

The pins at the head of the pelt should then be released and then those at the shoulders. The pelt should be trimmed to eliminate the slight flaps at the hips, and then formed with pins down both sides into the shape of a paddle blade.

After the pelt is pinned and tagged, it should be placed in a ventilated room or drying cabinet. The recommended temperature is from 55 to 60 degrees, with relative humidity from 40 to 50 percent. As the pelt dries, some fatty droplets may form, and they should be blotted up during the drying period, which takes about five days.

Most ranchers do not have special drying rooms.

One well known fur dresser recommends a pelt preservative to be used during the drying period.

Once the pelt has dried, the leather side may be brushed with a whisk broom, using care not to brush the front legs loose.

In spite of constant care, the fur side of pelts probably will need to be cleaned. This can be done with the regularly used dusting powder.

The fur should be laid leather side down on a clean, flat board, and a cup or two of the dusting powder or fine sawdust, placed on it.

This powder should be gently worked into the fur, and particularly around the upper edges that are the most likely to be dirty. This cleaning process should be continued until the fur is free from dirt and grease, and is fluffy.

Most of the cleaning powder can be removed by flipping the fur. The balance can be removed by very gently tapping the fur with a stick as you might beat a rug.

The pelts should be completely free of both dirt and the cleaning powder before they are shipped. Pelts to be shipped should be stacked in the following manner and shipped in firm containers. A piece of cardboard should be used as a base, and a pelt placed leather side down. The next pelt should be placed across the first, with the head going toward the rump of the first pelt. An additional layer of cardboard or paper should be put down before another two pelts are packed in a similar manner. Pelts packed this way will not have the objectionable crimped marks.

Pelts should be packed leather to leather and fur to fur.

When using the chloroform method, cotton is placed in the bottom of the jar and a small amount of chloroform poured on the cotton. A board is placed on top of the cotton to protect the fur.

Electrocution is the most widely used method of killing chinchillas. Terminals are attached to the tail and ear. 115 Volts are used. The current is turned on for about sixty seconds, and turned off for thirty seconds; then on again for sixty more seconds. One should be certain that the animal is dead before pelting. Wetting the tail and ear with salted water before attaching the terminals will make better contact.

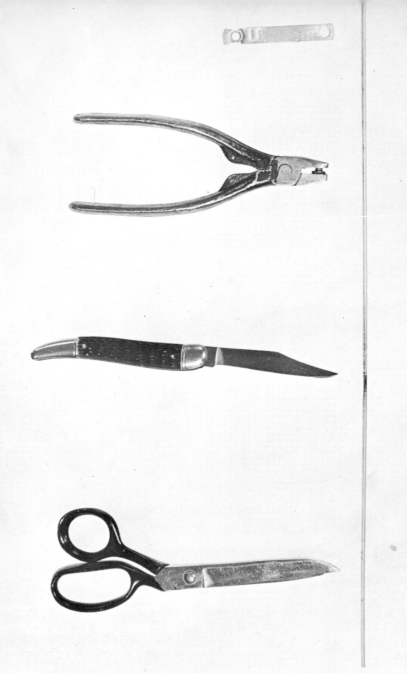

PELTING TOOLS

An umbrella stave or stiff wire; scissors or small pruning shears; a sharp knife; pelt tags; and pliers to fasten pelt tags.

Method of pelting illustrated and described on the following pages is one of a few methods in use.

128

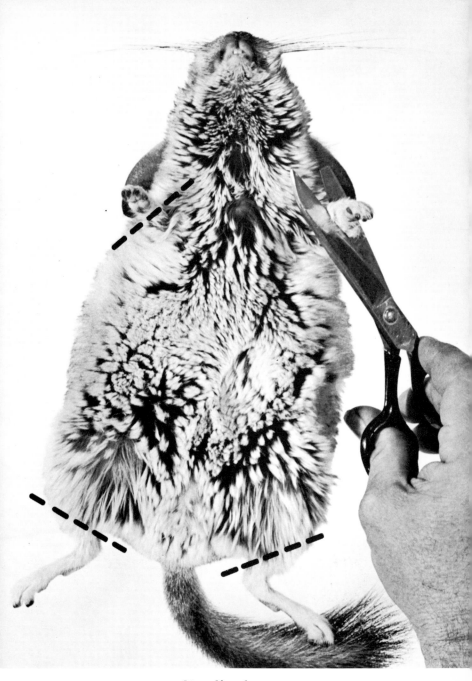

Step No. 1
Cut off hind legs, about ½ inch above hocks. Then cut off forelegs midway between wrist and elbow.

Step No. 2
Slit from base of tail to organs. Remove tail — about one inch from base. Slit lower ½ inch.

Step No. 3
Hold by the whiskers with thumb and index finger as the umbrella stave is inserted into slit in lower jaw and pushed through to organs. Still holding whiskers, place knife in groove of stave and slit back to the organs.

Step No. 4
Clip off the organs with scissors.

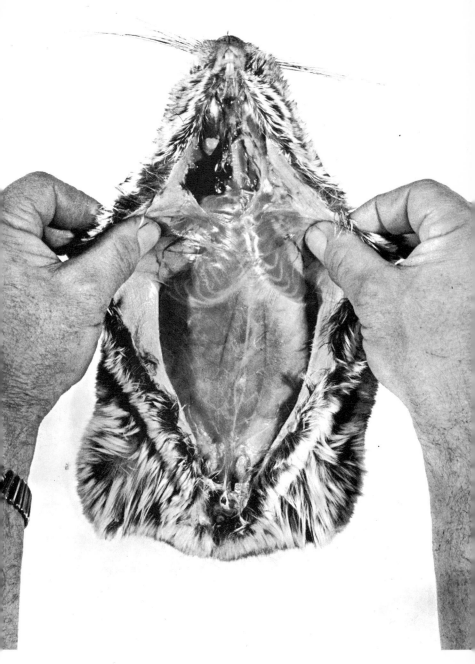

Step No. 5
Work carcass from the skin held by thumb and forefinger of right hand.

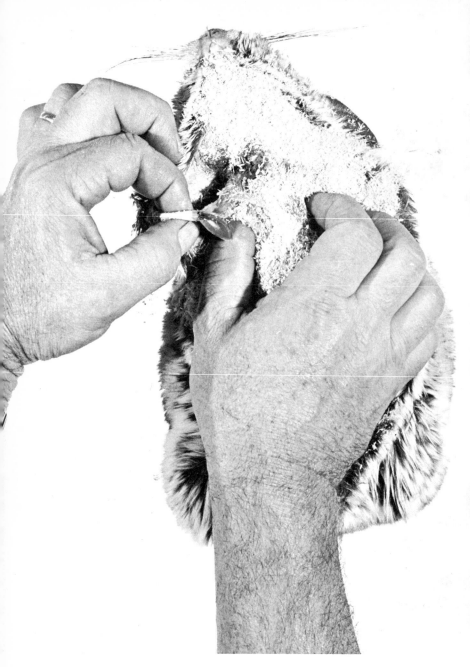

Step No. 6
Then left index finger under foreleg pulls pelt over the legs while carcass is held firmly around the trunk, using the right hand. At this point, sawdust should be put on the carcass to absorb body fluids.

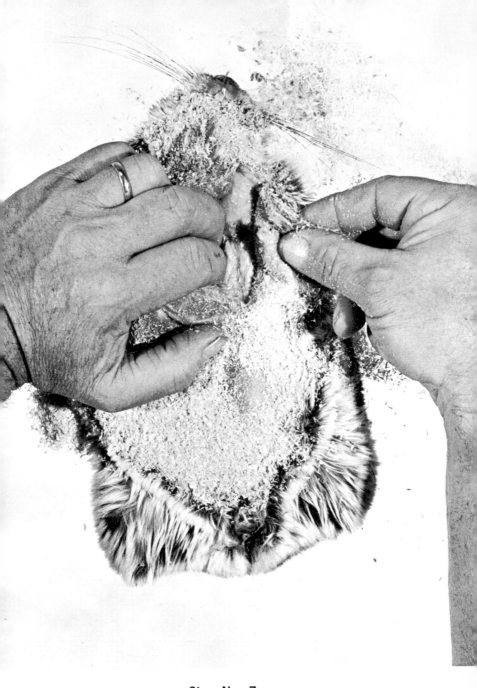

Step No. 7

Work fingers under the neck to separate pelt from the neck, shoulders and upper back.

Step No. 8
Back of the left hand holds the pelt while right hand pulls the carcass — free of the pelt to the hips.

Step No. 9
Put left hand under pelt and pull the carcass away with right hand
— the pelt pulls over hind legs.

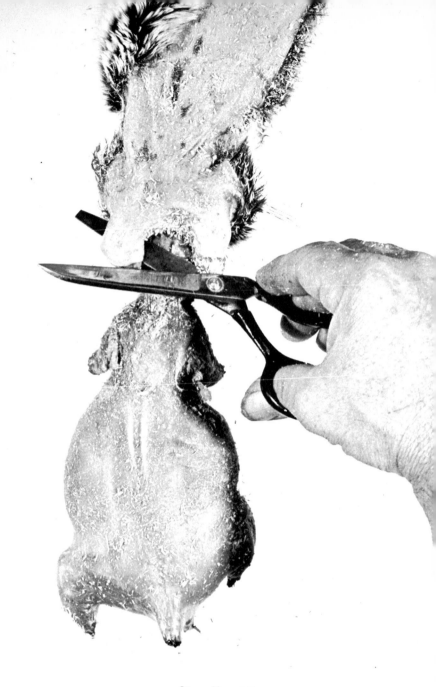

Step No. 10
Remove the pelt over the head, clipping ears, and pull down as far as front of eyes.

Step No. 11
Work pelt with forefinger and middle finger over head. Use the knife to free the pelt at front corner of the eyes.

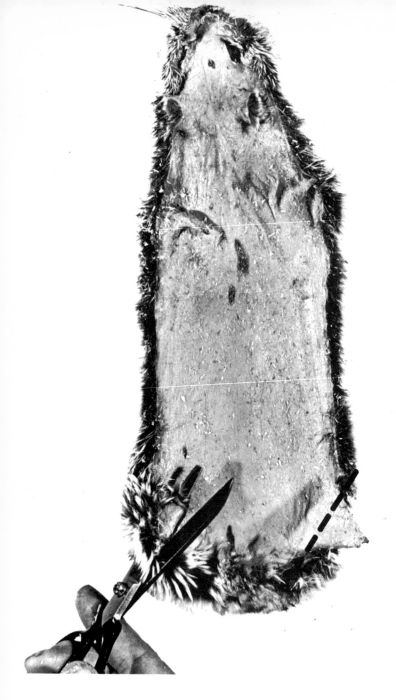

Step No. 12
Note placement of hind leg for opening tube — note trim lines.

Step No. 13
Position of the left hand while using fingers of the right hand to
flesh the pelt. After fleshing, brush up.

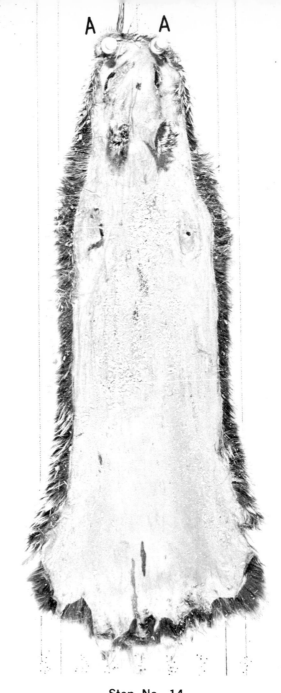

Step No. 14

Place pins at 'AA.' Brush in direction of arrows. Lift the pelt occasionally to prevent "laymarks."

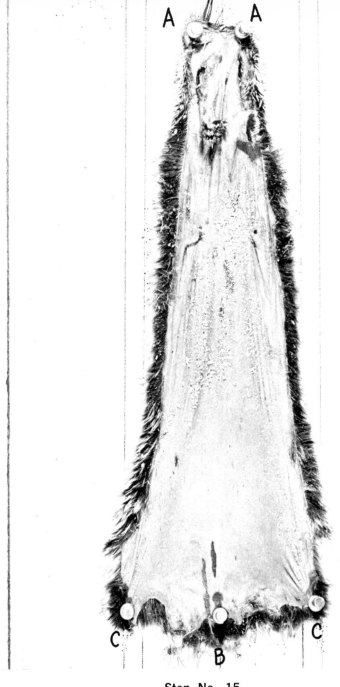

Step No. 15
While applying reasonable tension to the pelt, pin in center of base at 'B.' Also at 'CC' which will determine the base width.

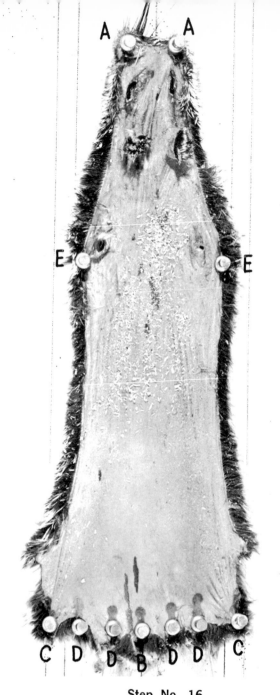

Step No. 16
Insert pins at points 'DDDD' to assume a final base shape. Then insert pins at 'EE' spreading the shoulders slightly, but ensuring that width at shoulders is less than that at the base.

144

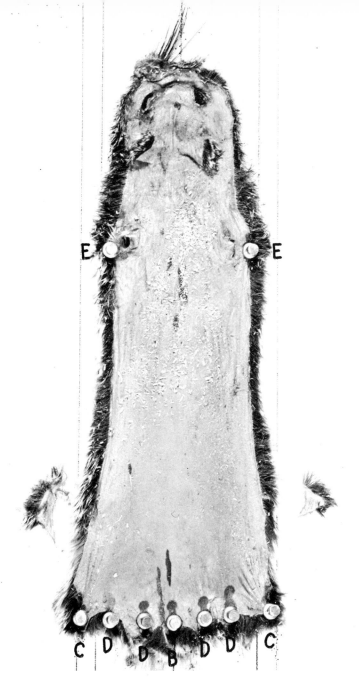

Step No. 17
Release pins along 'AA.' The head of the pelt will recede. Trim side tabs as shown.

← Point "A"

← Point "C"

Step No. 18

Now shape the pelt carefully to assume the final shape. Crowd shoulder area as much as possible without causing corrugation. Shape sides of pelts in very slight curves from Point A to Point C, not straight lines under tension. Replace pins as shown and allow to dry normally.

146

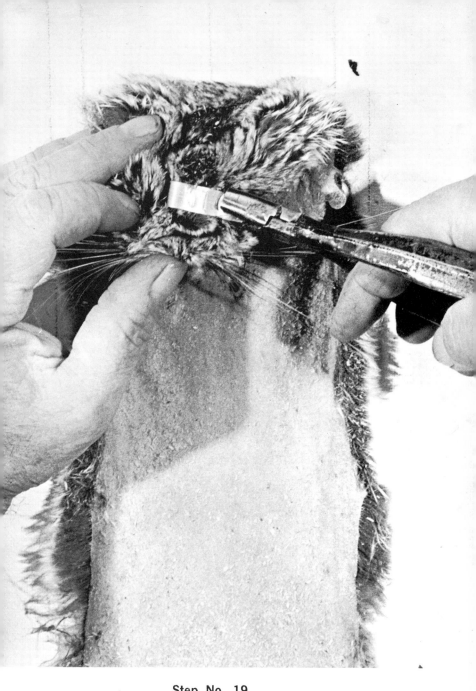

Step No. 19
The pelt tag can be put in the eye holes or the ear holes. However, it is best to put the tag in the ear holes, with the pelt tag number on the leather side of the pelt.

If there is the slightest danger of mice or other animals damaging the pelts, a drying rack can be enclosed with wire. The drying rack is enclosed with ¼ inch mesh wire, which will allow adequate ventilation.

Some of the larger ranchers will pin several pelts on a large beaver board and then place the board on a drying rack.

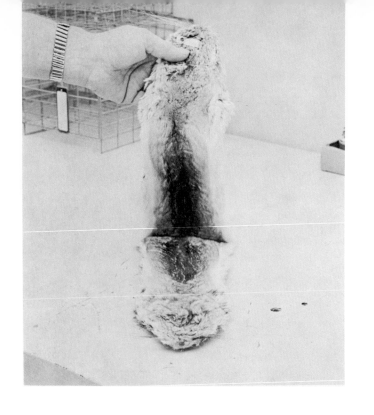

Care must be taken when packing pelts for shipment. To prevent grease burns, the pelts must be arranged fur to fur side, and leather to leather side. It is best to pack pelts in a cardboard box. Precaution should be taken that the pelts are not packed loosely. Packing pelts loosely can cause crimp marks.

Chapter XI   FUR DRESSING

One of the biggest obstacles the chinchilla industry had to overcome was in recapturing the art of chinchilla fur dressing.

In the latter part of the 1910's chinchilla became practically extinct. It wasn't until the 1940's that ranchers started to place emphasis on the marketing of pelts, thus leaving a span of more than 30 years of inactivity in chinchilla fur dressing.

The only place the chinchilla rancher could turn was to dressers of other furs. Numerous fur dressers were tried all over the world with disastrous results. It was not uncommon to have 70 percent or more of the pelts ruined. Many of the chinchilla pelts were dressed in Europe, and then shipped to the United States to be sold. All of this led to extensive research, hoping that the right process would be discovered. None was found. Just as it is today, each fur dresser had his own methods, and they were kept secret, and the secrets apparently passed away with the early day fur dressers.

After much trial and error, it was not until the early part of the 1960's that dressing of chinchilla pelts reached the point of consistent quality where it could be said "the art has been recaptured."

Many chinchilla ranchers use the word "tanner" in referring to a fur dresser. This is a misnomer, for while a tanner has a single purpose of processing leather only, the dresser has a twofold purpose. He must give protective treatment to both hide and hair. Since these substances have different physical and chemical reactions, he must employ a method of processing in which the one is not harmed during treatment of the other. Each kind of fur requires a different process. Therefore, the fur dressers' task is more complex than other related fields. Dressing chinchilla requires over forty separate operations. The dresser must cleanse and preserve the fur so that it will retain its strength, natural color and luster over prolonged usage in the finished garment.

In processing of chinchilla, special techniques must be used to prevent shedding. These techniques require more time and labor, and are not compatible with fast-leather manufacturing used in some fur dressing formulas.

If, for instance, a mink dressing process or mink dressing machinery were used on chinchilla, serious damage would result. The dresser must produce a leather that has strength and pliability that meet manufacturing requirements. The leather must also stand up with aging and wear.

While the most up-to-date equipment and the best chemicals are used, the success of dressing still depends upon the experience and knowledge of the people employed in this operation. Most of the processing must be done by skilled workers.

A chinchilla rancher need not make an extensive study of the technical aspect of fur dressing. However, it would be to his advantage to know some of the basic processes and problems of fur dressing.

It is important that something of the conditions found in the skin and hair be understood. The skin of animals used for fur consists of two parts—epidermis and the dermis. The epidermis or top skin has two parts—the outer layer and an underlying group of layers. These underlying layers consist of a sort of network of round soft cells which continually push up and become transformed in the flat, horny cells of the top layer. These horny cells are continually being shed as soon as they become very flat and dry.

The lower skin, or dermis, consists of many interwoven fibers that are rather white in appearance. These fibers are made of numerous thin, fine threads which are held together in a compact mass by a gelatin-like substance. The follicle from which hair begins its growth rests within the lower skin or dermis.

As stated previously, many hairs grow from a single follicle of chinchilla. Chinchilla is related to the porcupine family; therefore, the hair in the follicle is not anchored as tightly as in other fur-bearing animals. Consequently, the pelter must use special techniques in handling the live chinchilla and during the pelting operation. If the pelt is properly handled, the fur dresser will set the fur tightly in the initial stage of dressing. It is then permanently anchored for the life of the pelt.

To tan or dress skin into leather, all the blood cells, fatty tissues, and connective substances must be removed by scraping and washing so that only the fibers and horny cells remain. To prevent adhesion of these fibers into the formation of a hard, glassy mass, and also to prevent bacteria from entering and causing decay, preparations must be worked into the skin. This process converts the fibers and cells into leather and lubricates them so they will move freely.

The dressing process, besides preserving the skin, cleanses the fur and makes it lustrous by bringing out its natural beauty. It is best to dress chinchilla pelts in lots of 500 or more. It usually takes several owners' pelts combined to make lots of this size. Careful records must be kept on each owner's pelts so that they can be segregated after dressing. Ranchers should place identification fur seals on their own pelts. After lots are made up, the various processes of dressing are immediately started.

It is impossible to over-emphasize the importance of raw pelt preparation. Improper handling at the ranch level has cost ranchers thousands of dollars.

The following photographs, showing the four major processes in dressing chinchilla, were taken at Lloyd Sullivan's fur dressing plant in Oakhurst, California.

Several ranchers' pelts are dressed at the same time. Each rancher is assigned an identification number. The pelts are perforated with the assigned number, making it possible to segregate the pelts after dressing.

The **primary process** is considered the most important phase. The pelt is soaked in solutions which relax the leather and set the fur. After the pelts are relaxed and the fur is set, the pelts are then fleshed, removing excess fat and membrane.

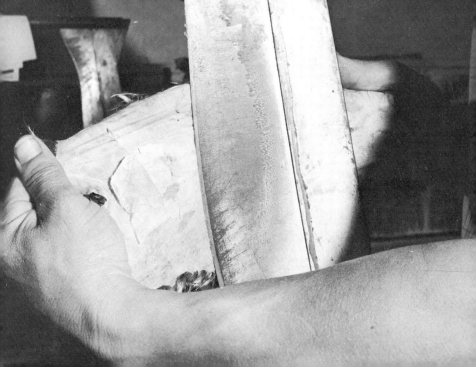

The next step is the **converting process.** After fleshing, the pelts are put into a solution which causes the pelts to swell, allowing penetrating chemicals to coat the fibers and fibriles, preventing adhesion and decay. During this process chemicals are also used to give the fur water resistant qualities. The pelts are then removed from the vats and prepared for oiling. A specially prepared mixture of vegetable and animal oils is swabbed on the leather side. The pelts are then stacked leather to leather, allowing the oils to penetrate into the leather. **Drying process.** The drying process is accomplished by placing the pelts on a rack in a room with controlled temperature and humidity, until the pelts are dry.

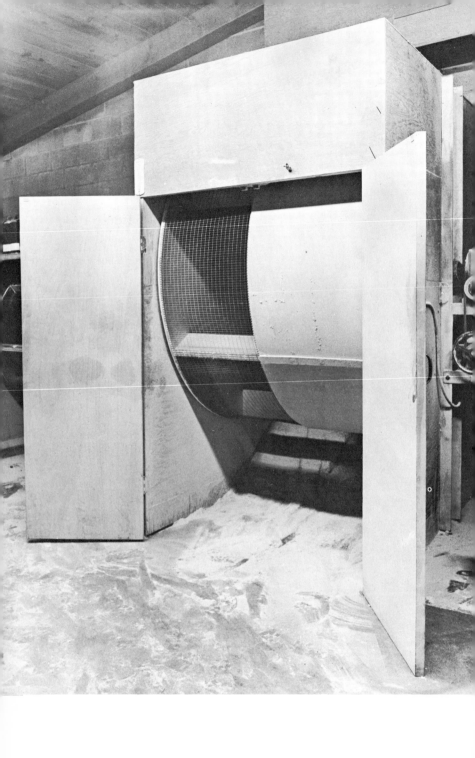

Finishing process. After the pelts are dried, the excess oil is removed. This is accomplished by putting the pelts in large drums with a hardwood sawdust. It requires three or more separate drummings, with fresh sawdust in each drumming, which takes several hours, depending on the condition of the pelts.

It is interesting to note that in the mid-fifties the New York Auction Co. felt that one of the drawbacks to the sale of chinchilla pelts was the casty and off color condition of many of the pelts.

Renaldo Pepi, a fur dresser from South San Francisco, California, realized the necessity of overcoming this problem and commissioned a chemist to assist in developing a process that would bring out the clear color of the fur and do away with the yellowish-brownish cast without affecting the true color of the fur itself.

The result of this research was an optical brightener which was formulated in Europe in the thirties but was not introduced into the United States until after World War II.

Optical brightener intensifies colors and makes them more brilliant.

There are some ranchers who feel that brighteners are no longer needed due to the fact that top quality chinchilla pelts can stand on their own merit.

In the late forties and early fifties vigorous efforts were made in dyeing and bleaching chinchilla with successful results. The dyed and bleached chinchilla pelts stimulated no interest in the fur market, making the value of such pelts practically worthless.

After the pelts are dressed, each pelt is given a final inspection before being shipped.

Chapter XII MARKETING

There are two major marketing organizations for the sale of chinchilla pelts: Empress Chinchilla Breeders Cooperative, Incorporated, and United Chinchilla Associates, Incorporated.

Each organization charges a fee for the sale of the pelts, and a minimum fee or percentage of the sale price of the pelt is retained for promotion of garment sales.

Unlike some other furs, chinchilla pelts are not sold in the raw. They are sold after they are dressed.

Many ranchers recommend that after dressing, the pelts should be returned to the rancher for valuation before the pelts are sent to the market. It would seem that this step could be one of the better ways for a rancher to determine the quality of the pelts being produced, and also assist in the valuation of herd improvement.

As shown in the chapter on pelting, an identification tag is placed on the pelt. The number of this tag should be recorded in the Herd Book, making it possible to trace the background of any pelt.

One of the bigger problems in the chinchilla industry is the poor quality pelts that are being sent to market. The marketing organizations of United Chinchilla Association and Empress Chinchilla Breeders Cooperative have programs to help overcome what appears to be an insurmountable problem. In the latter part of 1968, United Chinchilla Association opened an office in Millbrae, California, which is referred to as a clearing house. The activity of this office is to evaluate pelts before they are sent to market.

Raw pelts are refrigerated, kept at about 10° above zero. It is not necessary to refrigerate dressed pelts.

There is no minimum on the number of pelts which may be sent to market. Some ranchers believe that if just one pelt is sent to market, they will receive less money for it. This is not true. When pelts are received at the market, each pelt is graded on its own merit and put into matched bundles. The number of pelts in a bundle varies. There may be just a few, or there may be fifty or more.

The marketing company keeps track of each pelt, and when the bundle is sold, the rancher receives his share of the sale price.

Before the rancher receives payment for his pelts, the New York Auction Co. will send him a valuation sheet stating the lot number of the bundle in which the pelt was placed; the valuation of the pelt (how it was graded); and an estimate as to what it will sell for.

AURORA CHINCHILLA

(*The Ultimate Fur*)

UNITED CHINCHILLA ASSOCIATES, INC.

REJECT SLIP

Date_____

The following faults are noted (by an X) on pelts received from _____*John Doe*_____ upon examination. This does not guarantee that we have not missed additional ones. This criticism is offered in an attempt to help ranchers to produce finer skins.

PELT NUMBER	123	124	127	129		
Slipped Fur			X			
Matts						
Pen Stain						
Off Color	X	X				
Chewing						
Small Size						
Collar Damage						
Neck Density	X					
Overall Density		X		X		
Unprime				X		
Poor Veiling	X	X				
Tears in Leather						
Grease Burn						

REMARKS:_____ *Generally shaped too wide at shoulders*

Pelting Job: Poor _____. Follow Pelt Pattern.

Shaping of Pelt: Poor _*some leather strain.*_____. Seek Instruction.

ALL REJECT PELTS WILL BE RETURNED TO THE SHIPPER IF THE ASSOCIATION IS NOTIFIED WITHIN 90 DAYS FROM RECEIPT OF THIS NOTICE PROVIDING ANY SHIPPING CHARGES AND/OR DRESSING FEES DUE HAVE BEEN PAID.

If a pelt is rejected, it will be returned with the reject slip, upon the rancher's request. It would appear that such a service could help the rancher produce better quality pelts.

UCA CHINCHILLA GRADING CODE

Color Phase	Code	Clearness	Code	Quality	Code	Size	Code	Damage	Code
Light	1	Clear to Blue	1	Ex. Hvy. & Hvy.	1	Ex. Lge. & Lge.	1	Good Finish	0
Medium Light	2	Second	2	Semi-Heavy	2	Medium	2	Fair Finish	1
Medium	3	Third	3	Semi-Heavy (With Weak Neck)	3	Small	3	Rough Finish (Or Priming Lines)	2
Medium Dark	4	Off Color	4	Flat	4	Kit	4	Slight Slippage (Or Slight Damage)	3
Dark	5	Badly off Color	5	Assorted	5	Assorted	5	Serious Damage	4
Assorted	6	Assorted	6						

Example of code in use 4 2 2 1 0

Med. Dark 4

2nd. Color 2

Semi-Heavy 2

Extra large and large 1

Good Finish 0

Verbal Reference — LARGE MD 2

168

New York Auction Company.

226 WEST 26TH STREET

NEW YORK. N. Y. 10001

WA tkins 4-2990

	SALE DATE			DATE		
	MO.	DAY	YR.	MO.	DAY	YR.

PART LOT ADVICE

JOHN DOE
HILLTOP CHINCHILLAS
243 CREST ROAD
DES MOINES, IOWA

PREVIOUS LOT NO.	ARTICLE		LOT NO.	QUANTITY	VALUATION	
51111	PELT	17730	13800	1	35	00
42211	PELT	17717	13740	1	28	00
42211	PELT	17704	13740	2 T	28	00
31553	PELT	17669	13781	1	13	00
32211	PELT	17606	13797	1	21	50
41553	PELT	17714	13798	1	16	00
51110	PELT	17716	13852	1	35	00
33211	PELT	17738	13812	1	17	00

Prior to sending payment for sold pelts, New York Auction Company sends a valuation sheet which is an estimate of what price the pelts were sold for. The first column is the pelt valuation (how the pelt was graded). See chinchilla grading code on opposite page. The second column shows the pelt tag number. The third column shows the lot number in which the pelt was sold. The fourth column shows the number of pelts sold in the lot; "T" indicates the total number of pelts sold in a particular lot. The fifth column valuation is an estimate of approximately what the pelts sold for; not the true selling price. However, the actual selling price is usually higher.

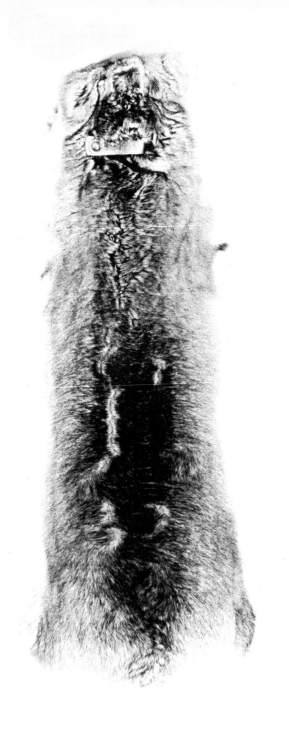

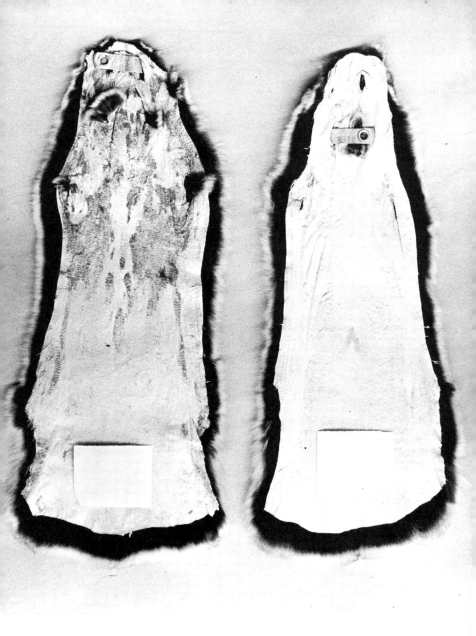

The pelt on the opposite page would appear to be a good pelt to the inexperienced eye. It was properly primed and pelted, and has good color. However, it is a low quality pelt. Notice the break in the fur and swirls. Above photograph, a comparison between a primed pelt and an unprimed pelt — the primed pelt is clear in color.

The above photograph is a graphic illustration of a good quality pelt.

Chapter XIII   RECORD KEEPING

Good ranch practice calls for two kinds of records. One set of records is on the animals themselves. These records are necessary not only for a herd inventory or census, but also to be used in planning breeding programs.

The second set of records is financial, and its purpose is not only for evaluating profit and loss, but also for tax purposes.

Initially, when the rancher has only a few animals, it may seem that records are hardly necessary, since most facts can be remembered. In this direction lies disaster.

The United States Department of Agriculture has estimated that more than 50 percent of all new farm failures are the result of poor record keeping, leading to a lack of knowledge on the part of the farmer as to his true financial condition.

Records need not be complicated in the small ranching operation. It should be immediately observed that because of the complexity of tax regulations, an accountant's services are advisable for any ranching operation.

In starting, the rancher can undoubtedly make use of one of the accounting systems available for small businesses at business supply stores. In keeping both animal and financial records, the important consideration is to be methodical and accurate.

Animal records are literally the accounting of animals, and they all have as their source the animals themselves. This means that the animals must be distinguished from one another in some manner. This is almost uniformly done in the industry through the tattoo and ear tags.

The tattoo or tag in the ear of the animal is used for identifying it throughout its life, and is also used on pedigree records for its progeny.

The tattoo provides a positive identification for each animal. The practice in the industry is to use a ranch brand in the left ear, and to put a letter denoting the year of birth, and the sequential number of birth in the right ear. The two tattoos thus provide identification for what ranch bred the animal, and to the breeder, what animal.

The Empress Chinchilla Breeders Cooperative, Inc, has developed a brand registration available to members, and United Chinchilla Associates, Inc. also maintains a registry of brands. Ranchers should register their brands, particularly if they intend to sell breeding stock.

The system established for year of birth is a letter system. The letter A stands for 1954, and the cycle is continued until 1973, when the letter A is used again. Thus an animal born in 1967 would have the letter R in its right ear, followed by the number of its birth, such as 5, if it were the fifth birth on the ranch in 1967.

Animals can be entered in a herd register which includes their brand number, the date of their birth, their sex, their dam and sire, and other pertinent information, such as their cost, if they are acquired animals.

Another animal record should be a pen card, which can be kept on the cage of the animal. This card can follow the animal through its life cycle, and be filed at the pelting or death of the animal. It provides information on the successful breedings of the animal and most breeders would probably want to record remarks on the animal; including the plan for breeding it, based on its strong traits.

The young animals are usually tattooed at the time they are weaned. There are several methods, ranging from a fountain pen tattooer to electric needles. For the small ranch, the fountain pen type of equipment is easy to use. It has a needle, instead of a pen point.

The tattoo is placed in the animal's ear by puncturing either part, or all the way through, and placing ink under the skin. It is relatively painless, and virtually permanent.

The ranch financial records can be any one of several different kinds, depending on the size of the ranch operation. The important thing is that the records be complete enough to be used not only for a measurement of expenses and income, but also to provide tax information.

A significant feature of the tax law is that permitting income from animals in the "Breeding" herd to be sold for capital gains, rather than having such income taxed as ordinary income. It is necessary, however, to prove to the revenue department that the animals were for breeding purposes, and have been retained in the herd over 12 months.

Most of the simple tax systems used by the small rancher will have in addition to the checkbook and bank book two types of journals; one for expenses, and one for income. Every transaction affecting the ranch can be entered in these two journals, and they provide the basis for more elaborate record systems if needed.

By using such journals it is possible to break down expenditures for animals, housing, equipment, feed, and labor, which provide a source for analyzing ranch operations.

The following list includes the most common expenses incurred by chinchilla ranchers.

Hired labor.

Feed and Supplies purchased.

Repairs & Maintenance of buildings and equipment.

Breeding fees.

Veterinary and medicine.

City and County taxes on animals, buildings and equipment, business licenses.

Truck and Auto expense.

Depreciation on purchased breeding animals; buildings and equipment.

Scoring, grading, and tattooing fees.

Advertising and business promotion.

Insurance on animals, buildings and equipment.

Interest paid in connection with the purchase of animals and equipment.

Water, electricity, and telephone.

Rent of grounds, buildings, and equipment.

Legal and accounting fees.

Office supplies and expenses.

Association dues and meeting expenses.

Registration fees.

Entry fees at animal shows.

Traveling expenses.

Business entertainment.

Dressing and pelting expenses.

In connection with items which include both business and personal expenses such as water, electricity, telephone, and auto expenses, some reasonable basis for allocation must be used. This basis will vary from one rancher to another depending on the circumstances.

Based on these journals, the rancher can at any specific time discover what his gross income on operation is. From this gross it will be necessary to deduct capital costs and taxes to obtain a net income figure. The rancher who is able, at any time, to calculate the financial position of his operation, is the rancher who should be successful.

Again, the single most important practice in record keeping is to do it regularly; certainly not less than once each week. In the instance of expenses and income, it will probably be easiest to make journal entries each day.

With even simple records, the rancher will be able to go to his accountant or attorney and get the most favorable type of tax return. Without records the rancher has little opportunity to take advantage of those tax provisions working in his favor.

A desk on wheels is an ideal piece of equipment on any ranch. Offering many advantages, it is a good place to keep animal and ranch records, storage for such items as pen cards, ear tags, tattooing kit, small tools, medicines, and odds and ends that have a habit of disappearing.

OWNER _____   FEMALE _____

Date Due	Sire	Date Littered	F	M

Date Born _____

❋ (   )

Dam ❋ (   )

Dam ❋ (   )

Sire ❋ (

Sire ❋ (   )

Dam ❋ (

Sire ❋ (

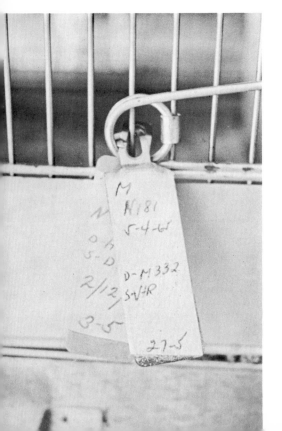

Pen cards vary in size and design, but contain the same basic information. Most ranchers will use a color code, such as pink cards for females, blue for males, and white for pelters.

Left: Plastic tag which serves the same purpose as a pen card, but clips on to the cage.

178

HERD BOOK

Ranch _____   Dates From _____ To _____

Birth Date	Sex	Brand	No.	DAM Brand	DAM No.	SIRE Brand	SIRE No.	Remarks	Date Pelted	Valuation	Sale Price
5/4	M ②	C/M	V 87	O/L	574	MP	P26	SILVER			
"	"	"	V 88	"	"	"	"	STANDARD			
5/8	F ①	"	V 89	c/M	R66	HT	R 12	BREEDER			
5/12	M ③	"	V 90	O/L	R 52	O/L	S 25	PELTER	3/18	33412	25.50
"	F	"	V 91	"	"	"	"	BREEDER			
"	F	"	V 92	"	"	"	"	DIED			

An accurate herd book is just as important as accurate financial records. First column — date of birth. Second column — sex and number of babies born in the litter. Third column — the brand. Fourth column — the letter of the year in which the baby was born (see page 184), and the number of the baby born in that year. Fifth and sixth columns — the brand and number of the dam and sire. Other information is also put in dam and sire columns. For instance, if the sire is a silver mutation a dot can be used to indicate it; or an "X" for beige, etc. Seventh column — remarks. Eighth column — date pelted. Ninth column — pelt valuation if sold through UCA (see page 168). Tenth column — sale price of the pelt, or the sale price if sold as a breeder.

Expenses

Date	Amount	Item	Feed & Supplies	Travel	Building & Material	Membership Fees	Misc.
Feb. 6	2000#	Hay	46.00				
6	500#	Pellets	35.25				
15		Club Meeting				1.25	
16		Office Supplies					2.78
17	5 doz.	Flash Cards					1.20
20	1 roll	Wire			17.20		
20	10#	Nails			1.25		
21	50 mile	to Rock Spring		5.00			
23	1	Magazine Subscription					6.00
25	10	Entry Fee Animal Show					20.00
25	75 mile	La Porte		7.50			
25		Entertainment					12.50
27	150#	Dust	11.00				
			92.25	12.50	18.45	1.25	42.48

Any money spent related to the ranch operation is considered expense. Therefore, all such items should be entered in the ledger under "Expenses." It is also of the utmost importance to keep all receipts and cancelled checks in the event that doubt should arise. Items such as buildings and capes which will be used over the years will have to be depreciated, and should be listed separately. With complex tax

Date		Item	Pet Sales	Live Animals	Feed & Supplies	Services Rendered	Misc.
Feb. 5	15	Pets	328 76				
10	3	Female		450 00			
10	1	Male		175 00			
10	1	Male		225 00			
10		Delivery Animals					15 00
13	100#	Pellets			9 50		
15	1	Bank of Cages			35 00		
16		John Doe				20 00	
10	10#	Supplement			2 00		
18	12	Pet Cords			36		
25	3	Animals Boarded					4 50
			328 76	850 00	46 86	20 00	19 50

All money received should be entered in the ledger under "Income."

QUARTERLY SUMMARY

Income   _Expenses_

| | CASH RECEIVED FROM: | | 2 | 3 | 4 | 4-A |
| YEAR 19___ | 1-A | 1-B | 1-C | TOTAL CASH RECEIVED | PAID OUT BY CASH | PAID OUT BY CHECK | TOTAL PAID OUT |
	Pelts	Bredng	Misc.				
Month of January	271 22	570 00	93 61	874 83	130 76	57 63	188 39
Month of February	328 76	850 00	86 36	1265 12	126 42	40 51	166 93
Month of March	815 15	725 50	213 25	1753 90	85 50	30 40	115 90
TOTAL—First Quarter	1415 13	2065 50	393 22	3893 85	342 68	128 54	471 22
Month of April	525 00	950 00	175 50	1650 50	98 40	60 32	158 72
Month of May	160 50	850 00	125 00	1155 50	14 80	26 00	167 80
Month of June	266 41	575 00	75 50	916 91	76 30	15 20	91 50
TOTAL—Second Quarter	971 91	2375 00	376 00	3722 91	316 50	101 52	418 02

The quarterly summary is a synopsis of the income and expense ledgers. It enables the rancher to determine gain or loss each month, as well as every three months, quickly and accurately.

ASSETS AND LIABILITIES
AT BEGINNING OF YEAR
ASSETS

CURRENT ASSETS:

Cash on Hand .... _255.00_

Cash in Bank .... _323.42_

Notes Receivable .... _2,350.00_

Accounts Receivable .... _175.50_

Inventory Stock on Hand.............. _275.25_

TOTAL .... _3,379.17_

FIXED ASSETS:

Land .... _4,500.00_

Buildings .... _5,500.00_

Equipment .... _3,575.00_

Furniture and Furnishings..... .. .. _250.00_

TOTAL .... _13,825.00_

OTHER ASSETS:

Car ...... _2,300.00_

1/2 ton pickup ... _800.00_

Chinchillas .....16, _000.00_

TOTAL .... _19,100.00_

TOTAL ASSETS .... _36,304.17_

LIABILITIES

CURRENT LIABILITIES:

Notes Payable .... _2,550.40_

Accounts Payable .... _43.90_

TOTAL .... _2,594.30_

FIXED LIABILITIES:

Mortgages .... _3,250.00_

2nd mortgage .... _4,500.00_

TOTAL .... _7,750.00_

TOTAL LIABILITIES .... _10,344.30_

NET WORTH (Deduct Total Liabilities from Total Assets
and enter the difference here)........................ _25,959.87_

TOTAL LIABILITIES AND NET WORTH......... _36,304.17_

The balance sheet shows total assets and liabilities. By looking at the previous year's balance sheet it is easy to see what progress has been made.

YEAR LETTERS:

A.	1954	R	1967	H	197?		
B	1955	S	1968	J	198?		
C	1956	T	1969	K	198?		
D	1957	V	1970	L	198?		
E	1958	X	1971	M	198?		
F	1959	Z	1972	N	198?		
H	1960	A	1973	P	198?		
J	1961	B	1974	R	198?		
K	1962	C	1975	S	198?		
L	1963	D	1976	T	198?		
M	1964	E	1977	V	198?		
N	1965	F	1978	X	199?		
P	1966			Z	199?		

Letters are used to indicate the year in which the chinchilla was born. Number after the letter shows the number of baby born that year. For example: " V 45 " would indicate the animal was born in 1970; 45 would be the forty-fifth baby born in 1970. However, letters that could be mistaken for other letters are omitted. For instance: "O" could be mistaken for the letter "Q."

There are several methods used to identify chinchillas. Some ranchers use ear tags, while others prefer the tattoo. An ear tag usually contains the brand, year letter and number — all of which can be incorporated in one tag.

When tattooing is used, the brand is put in one ear, and the year letter and number in the other ear.

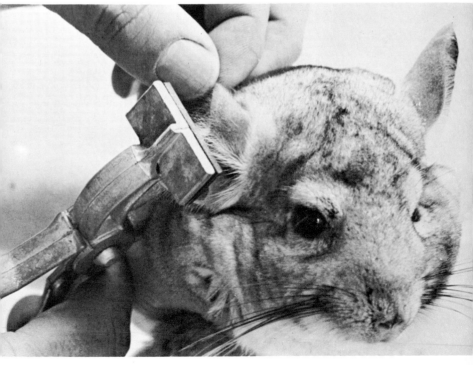

185

Chapter XIV   GENETICS

There are two systems of breeding: outbreeding and in-breeding. Therefore, it is necessary to understand the difference between the two.

Outbreeding is the mating of unrelated animals. For instance, if a male and a female are not related, their offspring are outbred.

Inbreeding is the mating of related animals. If a male and a female are related, their offspring are inbred.

Biologically, when any two animals have the same common lineage, they are related. Brothers are related because they have the same parents. Cousins are related because they have one pair of identical grandparents. The question then arises— how far back should ancestry be traced to determine if they are related. An accepted method is four generations. If there is an identical set of grandparents, great grandparents, or great, great grandparents, they are related. If, on the other hand, an ident-ical set of any of these is not found, it is considered they are unrelated.

Many ranchers do not search back for more than four genera-tions for a very good reason. The animal only furnished one half of its total inheritance to its offspring. That is, each parent contributes only one half of the total new biological cell.

Therefore, the law of inheritance becomes a process of halves. The fourth generation has 1/16th of the original parents, providing outbreeding has been practiced.

Outbreeding has some good effects and some bad. Outbreeding often tends to lend more vigor to the offspring. That is, the mixing of genes from unrelated animals may result in stronger offspring.

The drawback in the practice of outbreeding, of course, is the fact that the offspring cannot transmit a uniform line. The natural result would be considerable difference in the genetic structure of the species. It is reasonable to say that this form of breeding is more conservative, and would appear to be the best method for most breeders to practice until they fully understand inbreeding.

Inbreeding, on the other hand, if properly practiced, has nothing which is inherently harmful to the species. The result of inbreeding is the direct product of the genes contributed by the parents. Provided there are two parents of excellent quality, the breeder should institute the practice of inbreeding. Whether intense line breeding is used, (father to daughter; or brother to sister) should depend upon the number of desirable traits transmitted to the offspring.

Understanding the fundamentals of the art of inbreeding is a must for the breeder who wishes to engage in the actual practice. It should be known that both the desirable traits and undesirable traits will be accentuated more rapidly by inbreeding. Remember, it has been established—the mating of related animals will bring about uniformity in the species.

That uniformity, if not carefully guided, could result in downgrading the herd. Therefore, it should be determined beforehand exactly where the desired breed level is to be established.

How is it determined as to who should inbreed. Where individual breeders are concerned, there are times when they should outbreed, as well as times when they should inbreed. If a given herd is below average, then inbreeding could only result in continuing to produce below average animals. However, bringing in top quality sires should raise the quality level of the herd. This does not mean that all offspring in the given herd would increase to point of quality of the new sire. However, it would result in an introduction of higher quality genes within the herd structure.

It must be kept in mind that relationship measures the probability that individuals will be alike in their genes, and inbreeding is the most powerful tool a breeder has for establishing uniform quality animals.

There is one danger in intense inbreeding, and that is it could emphasize undesired genes at such a rapid rate, that it would be difficult to discard undesirable characteristics.

Line breeding is a form of inbreeding directed toward keeping the offspring more closely related to a highly admired ancestor or pair of ancestors. All inbreeding that does not hold this relationship high, must be avoided as much as possible. Therefore, the intensity of inbreeding is usually moderate in line breeding systems.

Relationship to a chosen ancestor is the main feature which distinguishes the line breeding system from other forms of inbreeding.

There are occasions when a breeder must resort to outbreeding. Outbreeding generally leads to individual excellence by careful breeding work. Continuous outbreeding will slow down further improvement of any individual herd because it destroys families by constantly crossing together any desirable characteristics which start to develop with undesirable genes from other bloodlines. Thus the herd may only be kept temporarily more uniform than if outbreeding were not practiced.

Cross breeding (mating of different varieties as, for instance, mating of a Lanigera and a Costina), is a special form of outbreeding where the parents belong to different varieties. It generally results in increased vitality, and sometimes fertility and size. The amount of this increase varies, according to the types of cross breeding used, and in some cases will show no increase at all.

The economy of cross breeding depends upon whether the increase in vitality, fertility and size is more than enough to balance the additional cost of replacements under a cross breeding system.

It is important to point out that simply mating "like to like" reaches the full limits of effects within a very few generations after it is begun. Such effects may disappear almost at once when random mating is resumed. The mating of unrelated animals may be useful in establishing and maintaining some uniformity in a herd until the average type, or some intermediate type, can be fixed and utilized by close inbreeding. Inbreeding may also be useful in correcting defects whenever the "ideal" animal is intermediate, and some animals are too extreme in both directions.

There are many problems facing the individual breeder, and these are usually encountered when planning the breeding program. These problems seem to center around the establishment of an ideal system for a rapid herd improvement; endeavoring to solve problems; and obtaining opportunities in the animal breeding field.

The system proposed for rapid improvement of a breed is dividing the herd into small groups, and practicing limited line breeding and some cross inbreeding in each group, making occasional exchange of various animals from different herds. That is, exchanging between two breeders of desirable sires, when it seems desirable. Both of these methods must be accompanied at all times by very careful selection.

It is most certainly beyond the scope of this chapter to cite all the ramifications of genetics, heredity, breeding, hybrids, and mutations. However, the same basic principles are involved.

The practical and professional rancher who intends to improve his stock should, in the area of genetics and heredity, approach it by valuating available stock; by having the courage to cull; and by keeping an accurate herd breeding record book at all times.

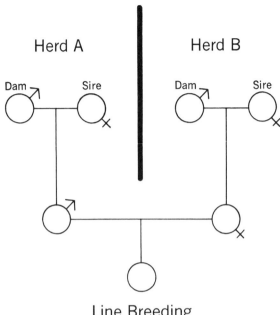

Line Breeding

Line breeding (outbreeding): Mating the same strain but with different genes. For instance: mating an animal from Herd "A" to an animal from Herd "B" which are of the same strain, but with different characteristics.

Inbreeding: Mating father to daughter; mother to son; or brother to sister.

Cross breeding: Mating different strains; such as mating a Brevicaudata with a Lanigera.

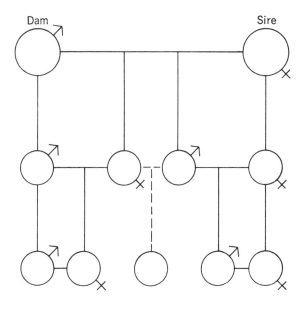

In Breeding

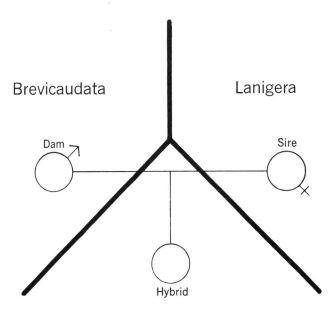

Brevicaudata

Lanigera

Cross Breeding

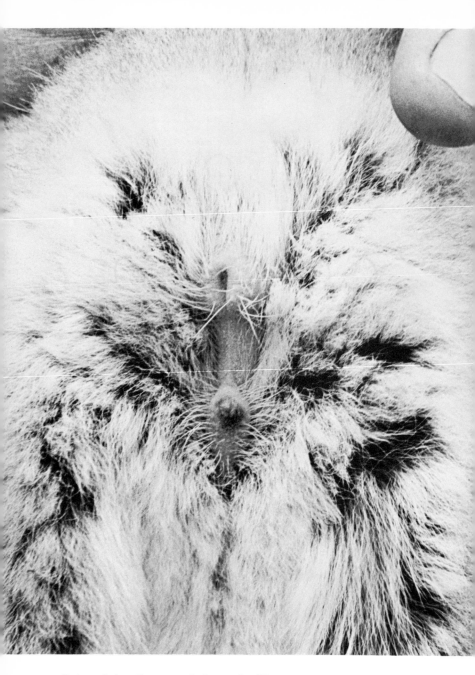

Determining the sex of the male. There are two protrusions about three eighths of an inch apart. Top protrusion is the anus, and lower protrusion the penis.

Determining the sex of the female. There are also two protrusions, but they are very close together; the anus and the vagina.

Chapter XV   ARTIFICIAL INSEMINATION

In the early part of the nineteen fifties energetic efforts were started in the development of artificial insemination and semen valuation. However, it was not until the latter part of the nineteen sixties that these efforts reached the point of consistency where they became practical on the ranch level.

Many ranchers feel that semen valuation is as important as artificial insemination. Ranchers have reported increases of one half a baby per year per female after all the males were sperm tested. This was after the males with low sperm count along with males with no active sperm were replaced with acceptable males.

When testing males for sperm count, it is equally important to check for a plug, which is a gelatin like substance that is ejected after the sperm. The purpose of the plug is to hold the sperm in the female until the sperm can reach and fertilize the egg in the female. Males that do not produce a plug have no place in the breeding herd.

There are many advantages in artificial insemination. One is: A rancher who desires to obtain offspring from a specific male can often obtain semen from the male and have his females inseminated.

Another advantage of artificial insemination is: A rancher who has an outstanding male can collect semen and inseminate (breed) females with which the male is not compatible.

The only time a female can successfully be inseminated is after giving birth. The best time for insemination is from twelve to twenty-four hours after littering. However, the female stays open about thirty-six hours.

Some ranchers inseminate once, twelve to twenty hours after birth; while others will inseminate twice. The first time about twelve hours after birth, and again about twelve hours later.

When determining the rate of conception, one must consider the time of the year. Higher percentages can be expected in the fall, when breeding is more pronounced than at other times of the year. Conception can vary from forty-five percent to eighty percent. However, sixty percent is considered good.

Artificial insemination and semen valuation are highly technical procedures requiring the services of a knowledgeable veterinarian or trained technician.

This does not mean the chinchilla rancher cannot be trained to become proficient in this particular field.

It must be remembered that it is a common practice in the cattle industry for breeders to do much of their insemination.

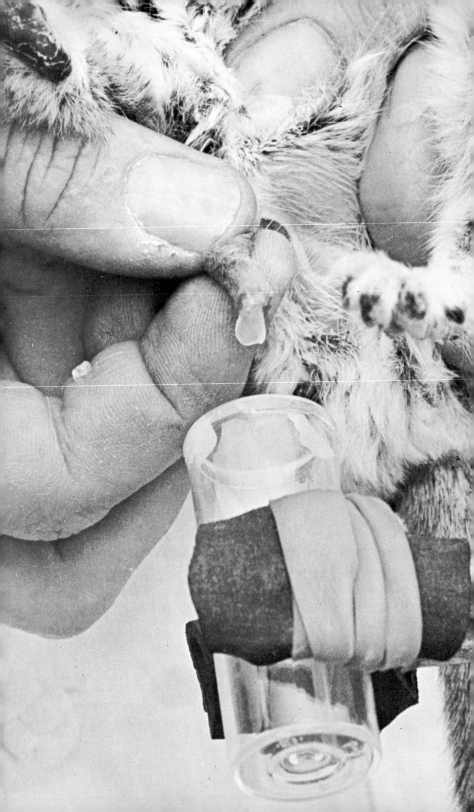

Three characteristics are checked when evaluating semen. Swirl, which is the amount of sperm; motility, the direction in which the sperm swims; and morphology, the shape of the sperm.

Most technicians recommend ejaculating chinchillas manually. It is important to check for the copulation plug, which is ejected after the sperm. The copulation plug holds the sperm in the female. Note: The gelatinous substance at the end of the penis is the copulation plug.

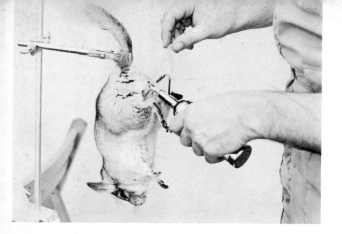

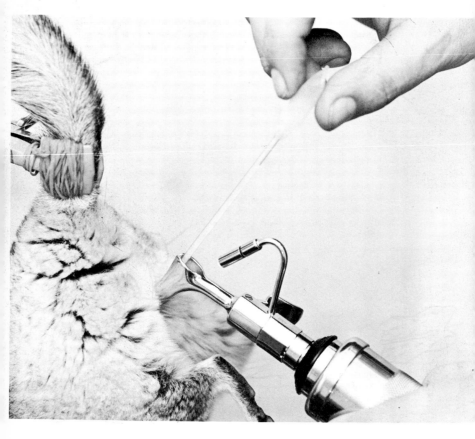

Insemination: The female is hung by the tail. A nasal speculum is used to open the vaginal cavity, and a glass cannula containing the semen is inserted. The semen is put into the horn of the uterus.

Copulation plug: Several hours after breeding, the female ejects
the plug. In the lower right corner is the plug; actual size — about
five sixteenths of an inch in diameter, and three fourths of an inch
long.

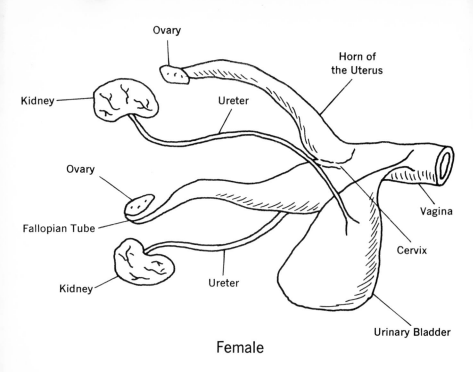

Female

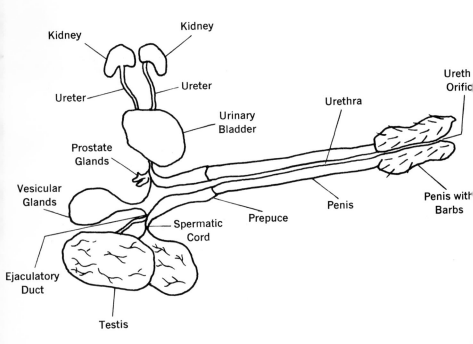

Male

Chapter XVI   DISEASES

The information in this chapter was approved by George Phillip Bertetta, D.V.M., of San Jose, California.

If chinchillas are properly housed, high standards of sanitation maintained, proper ventilation provided, and a well balanced diet fed — chinchilla problems should be almost nonexistent.

Full responsibility must be assumed by the rancher in the use of any treatment or medication mentioned in this book.

A veterinarian should be consulted under any circumstances.

ACCIDENTAL INJURIES to an animal can be the result of fighting, rough or incorrect method in handling, falls, and handling babies roughly. Also, catching a paw in the wire of the cage could cause lameness, and sharp objects in the cage can cause cuts.

SYMPTOMS: Injuries in animals are present if there is bleeding, lameness. If a paw is caught in the wire, care should be taken when removing the paw from the wire.

Care should be taken at all times to prevent escape of animals from cages.

SUGGESTED TREATMENT: Cut fur away from wound; clean with peroxide; apply antibiotic ointment; antibiotic injection.

PREVENTION: Handle animals carefully. Remove all sharp objects from cages. Prevent escape from cages. Use caution when catching a loose animal.

BLOAT is a condition that may be caused by moldy feed, and also may be caused by inability to chew food properly because of malocclusion or a respiratory disorder.

SYMPTOMS: Swelling of the abdomen; constipation; loss of appetite; dull eyes; shock.

SUGGESTED TREATMENT: Enema; peanut, soy, or corn oil by mouth, given very carefully to prevent inhalation into lungs; dose $\frac{1}{4}$ to $\frac{1}{2}$ teaspoonful three times a day.

PREVENTION: Be absolutely certain that feed is free of mold.

CONSTIPATION is infrequent passage of waste matter, and careful observation of droppings will indicate if this condition is present.

It can be caused by absence of muscular tone in the intestinal walls; nervousness; and infections; lack of roughage in diet.

SYMPTOMS: Small or no droppings; loss of appetite; dull eyes; listlessness.

SUGGESTED TREATMENT: Increase roughage. Relief may be provided by a mixture of equal parts of mineral oil and Milk of Magnesia given in doses of $\frac{1}{4}$ to $\frac{1}{2}$ teaspoonful twice a day until the droppings are normal.

PREVENTION: Adequate diet; fresh food and water; clean feeding utensils.

DIARRHEA is a disease which can be brought on by a number of conditions, most of which can be avoided, and it may also be the symptom of another problem.

Unsanitary housing; unsanitary feeders and watering system; sudden change of feed and water; poor ventilation and high humidity — these are all contributing factors that could cause this condition.

SYMPTOMS: Loose, soft, or runny droppings.

SUGGESTED TREATMENT: Isolation. Kaopectate, $\frac{1}{4}$ to $\frac{1}{2}$ teaspoonful every four hours, or more frequently if necessary. If not corrected in one to two days, consult veterinarian.

PREVENTION: Keep the chinchilla units clean. Be sure that all feeding utensils are clean. Be certain that all feed is free of mold. Provide good ventilation. Observation of droppings.

ENTERITIS is inflammation of the intestines. It is a contagious disease which can be caused by moldy feed and bacterial infections.

SYMPTOMS: Watery diarrhea; mushy droppings or constipation; listlessness; loss of appetite; rough coat; swollen abdomen; prolapsed bowels.

SUGGESTED TREATMENT: Same as for Diarrhea. Isolation. Kaopectate, $\frac{1}{4}$ to $\frac{1}{2}$ teaspoonful every four hours, or more frequently if necessary. If not corrected in one or two days, consult veterinarian.

PREVENTION: Isolation of new animals from herd. Keep units clean and well ventilated. Provide fresh food and water.

EYE INFECTION in chinchillas may come from physical or chemical irritants; also from infection or deficiency of Vitamin A.

SYMPTOMS: Swelling and redness around eyes; watering or pus formation in or around the eyes; eyes stuck closed; sensitivity to light.

SUGGESTED TREATMENT: Clean eyes with an eye wash; apply an antibiotic ointment.

PREVENTION: Avoid use of toxic chemicals. Sanitation.

FUNGUS is a surface growth of mold that flourishes in dampness and on decaying matter. It can often be found in feed that has molded and become contaminated. Fungus can be acquired by animals from spoiled hay, and from other animals that already have fungus.

SYMPTOMS: Loss of fur in patches; broken whiskers; muzzle red with scabs; loss of weight; languid behavior; rising temperature if systemic, internal (generalized fungus growth covering entire body).

SUGGESTED TREATMENT: Isolate. Cut or pluck hair away around lesions; wash with soap and water. Dry and apply Desenex ointment. Add Desenex powder to dust bath.
The dust bath and other contaminated material of affected animal should be carefully disposed of to prevent spread of the fungus. Herdsman should wash thoroughly after all handling of affected animals. Changing clothes is also advisable.

PREVENTION: Observe animals carefully when they are feeding. Look for loss of fur, broken whiskers; sterilize cages and equipment before using, and keep clean. See that hay and pellets are clean and fresh, and stored in clean, dry storage area. Destroy damp and contaminated hay and pellets by burning. Burn loose fur. Isolate and examine new animals for thirty days before they are moved in with the rest of the herd.

HEAT PROSTRATION is exactly what it implies; the animal falling down completely from excessive heat. Poor ventilation and high temperatures can cause heat prostration; also direct exposure to sunlight.

SYMPTOMS: The animal may be unconscious, and a high temperature will be present.

SUGGESTED TREATMENT: Move the animal to a cool place. If the animal is conscious, slightly salted cool water can be given. If the animal's temperature drops below normal, keep the animal warm. Also, ice packs may be used to lower the temperature, or sponge with lukewarm water, (not cold).

PREVENTION: Avoid direct sunlight on animals. Provide proper housing and ventilation. Provide air conditioning of chinchilla units. Regular check of air conditioning system.

MIDDLE EAR INFECTION is the result of bacteria brought in through the nasal passages to the middle ear passages.

SYMPTOMS of this condition are: Twisting and lowering of the head to the affected side; the animal runs in circles; when picked up by the tail it often rotates to the affected side.

SUGGESTED TREATMENT: Clean with medicinal Hydrogen Peroxide. When clean and dry apply antibiotic ointment. Antibiotics. Vitamins.

PREVENTION: Keep animals out of drafts. Prevent colds, which may result in ear infection.

MALOCCLUSION is a condition where the teeth do not come together to enable proper biting and chewing. This condition is believed to be inherited, and can also be caused by poor health and too frequent breedings. Since food cannot be chewed properly when malocclusion is present, the animal cannot obtain the full benefit from its food.

SYMPTOMS: Poor eating habits; loss of weight; watery eyes; constipation; pawing over food.

SUGGESTED TREATMENT: Keep teeth trimmed.

PREVENTION: Do not breed.

MASTITIS is an inflammation of the breast. It can be caused by babies biting the nipples when nursing; unused glands; weaning too soon; overproduction of milk.

SYMPTOMS: swelling and redness of breast; hardness of breast; the mother restless and uneasy while nursing.

SUGGESTED TREATMENT: Rub very lightly with Camphorated Oil for about three minutes, four times a day. Antibiotic if caked milk or breast is developing.

PREVENTION: File babies' teeth and fingernails. Close observation of mother while nursing babies, so that early detection of mastitis can be made.

PNEUMONIA, an inflammatory disease of the lungs, can be caused by drafts; humidity; eye, nose and other infections; dusty and damp litter material; and inhalation of dust or chemical irritants.

SYMPTOMS of this disease are: loss of appetite; very little or no droppings; difficult breathing; abdominal swelling; listlessness.

SUGGESTED TREATMENT: Antibiotics, steam inhalation, Vitamins to maintain resistance.

PREVENTION: Provide sanitary housing. Keep animals out of drafts. Check humidity and temperature in units regularly. Use a dehumidifier to keep humidity at proper level.

Courtesy Aurora Chinchilla

The author wishes to express his sincere thanks to all the wonderful people who so generously took time from their busy schedules to aid in the development of this book.